THE VISION OF THE PAST

PIERRE TEILHARD DE CHARDIN

THE VISION
OF THE PAST

TRANSLATED BY J. M. COHEN

HARPER & ROW, PUBLISHERS
New York and Evanston

CONTENTS

CHAPTER I

HOW THE TRANSFORMIST QUESTION
PRESENTS ITSELF TODAY

New truths are felt before they are expressed; and when they are expressed for the first time they are inevitably couched in a defective form. Appearing at their birth like a gleam in the night, they strongly attract us. Yet we do not know in what precise direction or on what exact level this source of brilliance lies. For a long time we fumble, colliding with many dark objects and deceived by many reflections, before we join the light whose rays are guiding us forward.

In order to make a fair judgement of transformist theories, we must remember that they have inevitably followed that law of progressive advance that governs the genesis of all new ideas. Though it is today indisputable that Lamarck, Darwin and their countless disciples in the nineteenth century saw a true light shining ahead of them, it is no less evident to us that, in the attempts they made to capture it many of their efforts went astray. The first generations of transformists were unable to define exactly what was essentially new about their theory, and also what was strictly biological in the unsuspected connections which they found within nature. They combined with their often masterly insights a great deal of defective explanation and false philosophy.

Have we in the last years come a little nearer to the truth behind Lamarckism and Darwinism? Can we today separate better than our predecessors those aspects of the idea of biological evolution that rightly attract our minds from those that draw them dangerously towards a deceptive light? In what terms does the transformist problem present itself today? The question is interesting, both for those who subscribe to transformism (and cannot always explain to themselves with sufficient clarity the reasons for their intellectual sympathies), and for anti-evolutionists (who often persist in concentrating their fire on abandoned positions).

The aim of these pages is to bring some partial answers which will enlighten adversaries and encourage friends.

Assuming a predominantly palaeontological viewpoint, I will try here to explain the form which the chain of organized beings appears to take, in the eyes of almost all contemporary scientists. And all that I shall say can be reduced to the following three points: 'In relation to the beliefs held by the initiators of the transformist doctrine, our present views of nature reveal a biological evolution (1) much more complicated in its process than was at first thought; (2) but at the same time increasingly certain as a fact; (3) provided that it is understood as a very general relationship of physical dependence and continuity between organized forms.'

A *Increasing Complexity of the Process Recognized by Science in Biological Evolution*

Like all scientific theories in their origins, biological evolutionism began by being extremely simple in its explanations. It had its golden age, during which it was thought possible to explain the distribution of living forms by drawing a relatively restricted series of zoological lines, completely separate from one another, and quick and continuous in their development.

All living and fossil animals, it was then thought, could be arranged on a small number of lines, along which increasingly complicated types replaced one another entirely in the course of time – all representatives of form N taking on the form of N + 1. The transformation of organisms on each line being continuous, and all the lines together forming a relatively simple sheaf, it was easy to mark precisely the empty places, that is to say to count the missing links on each living chain. This whole fan of forms, moreover, diverged and developed at appreciable angles and speed. Scientists flattered themselves, therefore, that they could easily discover the first origins and persistence until today of the movement of life. On the one hand, indeed, the various lines of animals, traced back into the past, must come together at a single and sensible point of morphological dispersion, lying in the region of the Cambrian. On the other, any reasonably careful experiments showed the malleability of organized matter. Not only the fact, but even the mechanism of evolution seemed clear; to explain the metamorphoses of life, it was enough to resort to natural adaptation or selection and heredity. Here, somewhat simplified, is the picture of transformism from Lamarck to Haeckel.

The discovery of new facts, and a regard for the truth before all else (which is, after all, the dominant quality of scientists) has perforce led in the last thirty years to some singular modifications in this much too approximate picture.

It has been noticed, in the first place, that many living series considered genealogical (phyletic) are only morphological, that is to say have only been established in regard to the variation of one particular organ. One animal at first considered the ancestor of another was later found to have lived contemporaneously with it; or it was even noticed that beside the 'adaptative' characteristics on which the genealogical relationship had been based, this animal showed some indications of positive divergence; if the paws, the teeth or the skull were no longer considered in isolation, but all these parts together, the second form could no longer be placed in a line of extension from the first. Two cases are well known: that of the *Hipparion,* at first regarded, on account of its three-toed foot, as the predecessor of the horse, but in reality, in the structure of its teeth, a more complicated creature; and that of the *Aceratherium,* more primitive than the rhinoceros by the absence of the horn on its nose, and yet contemporary with it. It would be easy to multiply examples of these early mistakes which have had to be corrected. After a closer study of fossil remains and stratigraphy, the species so neatly aligned by the first transformists have, very often in recent years, been moved into different relationship to one another; and instead of forming, as once, a regular curve, they are frequently arranged on either side of

9

an axis which has become somewhat theoretical as the divergent barbs of a feather along a central spine. At the same time as the lines once traced by transformism have been thus disintegrating under the analysis of the laboratory workers, new explorations have been revealing plentiful remains of absolutely new animals in the geological beds. And this has led perforce to a multiplication of families and zoological orders, that is to say has overloaded the design put together by the first palaeontologists. The leaves began to mask the twigs, and the over-numerous twigs more and more to hide the branches. Life thus tended to overwhelm the classifiers by the richness of its forms. It soon had to be admitted that its developments have been terribly capricious and immeasurably old.

It first became necessary to renounce the idea of a regular, continuous and total evolution. The *Terebratula* of our coasts, the *Lingula* and *Limulus* of the Pacific, the *Trigonia* of Australia, the cockroaches, the scorpions, etc, are creatures irremediably fixed, true living fossils, which have not departed in a single important feature from their type in the Secondary, the Carboniferous or even the Cambrian. While certain regions of the animal world were completely renewing themselves, others therefore remained strictly stationary. This is a curious fact. But what is even more disturbing is that the immobilized types which we find in nature are not only final twig-ends, species squeezed in a sort of morphological blind alley. The nautilus of the Indian Ocean, or the Syrian rock-badger, or the tarsier of Malaysia, or the *Cryptoproctus* and the lemuroids of Madagascar might, if known only in their fossil state, quite easily assume the role of genealogical intermediaries. Now all of them have remained living around us, unchanged for an immense period. The multiplicity of animal forms belonging to the same epoch of life is not, therefore, the only difficulty that plotters of genealogies encounter in their work. The interweaving of all sprigs born in a single spring is complicated by the survival of numerous archaic types, whose uniform shoots pierce the new verdure on all sides.

How far must we descend in the geological strata to reach the origin of these solitary stems? Sixty years ago, in describing the trilobites, it was possible to speak of 'primordial fauna'. Thanks to the celebrated discoveries of the American palaeontologist Walcott in British Columbia, we know today that the most ancient schists in the world (Algonkian) already contain very differentiated crustaceans; and in the middle of the Cambrian we can study, even in the detail of their soft parts, not only crustaceans belonging to all the great orders of today, but annelids and sipunculids like those now living, and some extremely specialized holothuroids. This 'tremendous discovery', as our author describes it, means that if by a miracle we were transported to the edge of the primal ocean, we should see creatures more or less like those that now inhabit our beaches crawling and running on sand and among rocks like those of our shores. Only the absence of birds on the sea and, perhaps, fish in the water – only a more careful examination of the crustaceans hiding under the boulders or in the pools might warn us of the terrifying descent our experiment had made into the past. In a considerable part of its fauna, the living world would seem to us as old as now. After journeying millions of years into the past, we should not have the impression of having come much nearer to the origins of life.

Contrary to what must have been the hopes of the first transformists, the centre of dispersion of living forms still therefore escapes us. It retreats further and further; and this backward movement is communicated to all the details of the evolutionary edifice. We now know mammals in the Triassic, bats and edentates in the lower Eocene, true apes in the Oligocene, etc. Everything in the life of the world is older than we thought. And everything is much more stable too.

Life, when we look at it for the first time by the light of the laws of transformation and adaptation, takes the form of a moving and flowing river, capable of shaping itself to all banks and slipping into all crevices. It is as if we had only to touch it, and we would feel it running through our fingers. Well, during the last half-century thousands of ingenious workers have submitted this material which seems so malleable to all sorts of internal and external modifications: hybridizations, traumatisms, various injections, everything has been tried. But we are still wondering whether it has really begun to yield even in a single case. Like the rocks, with their often gentle undulations, that contain its remains, life regarded as a whole and in its results, is an embodiment of simple and easy variation. Try to touch it: it breaks but does not bend.

Complexity, irregularity, great age, the apparent present stabilization of biological evolution, all these limitations imposed by the facts on the first conceptions of the transformists have been considered by the anti-evolutionists as so many defeats inflicted by nature on their adversaries. Their triumph is unjustified. Transformism has, of course, had to modify itself. It has had to correct its over-simple formulae by supplementary clauses. But let there be no mistake, these transformations have left it still intact; and at the present moment, one can say that it has a very satisfactory solution which interprets the facts.

Today natural scientists have abandoned the conception of a too simple and regular development of life. They admit that when it first appears before us, it is already very old; and this fact is amply explained to them by the well-proven recrystallization of the first sedimentary beds in enormous thicknesses. They now recognize that life, similar in this respect to a great tree or a great people, is transformed regionally and in jerks – here completely stuck for long periods, there brusquely awoken and beginning to grow again, and in another place still fresh and still climbing. They know too that within a single geological group only certain individuals can begin to change while the rest remain stationary, so that one sees the old types persisting for a long time beside the new. Because of the great number of species and the rarity of fossils, they despair of exactly reconstructing genealogies, line by line, and are content with an approximate seriation, which is all that is possible with the elements at their disposal. They would not be upset, in fact, if new reverses tended to prove that life is incapable of further variation on earth, either because its growing time is over, or because it grows so slowly, so spontaneously, or at periods so far apart, that we must abandon all hope of perceiving and, *a fortiori*, of ourselves modifying its movement.

This new transformism, mature in greater wisdom, is in perfect agreement with the dictates of experience. It is merely a question of finding in the biological domain the same contingencies and discontinuities that we observe everywhere around us in the development of individuals and civilizations. It has every appearance therefore of being a good explanation of reality. But, it will perhaps be objected: If we make all these saving concessions, does it not thereby become unverifiable? If the world of life is so obscure in its origins, so complicated in its structure, do we not become free to read whatever we want into its capricious outlines: transformism, of course, but many other things too?

To this objection we must reply with an unhesitating No. No, even corrected and attenuated by multiple limitations, the transformist interpretation of things (reduced to an essential element which will be defined later) is nevertheless the solution that seems to impose itself. More and more clearly, we must affirm (provided we stick to the empirical and historical plane of the Universe) it appears to be the only possible explanation of the morphological, temporal and geographical distribution of living beings.

B *Increasing Factual Confirmation of Some Kind of Transformism*

The adversaries of biological evolution often imagine that they have only to look at nature, never mind how and where, to judge the explanatory value of transformism. This is an elementary mistake of method. If geologists had not the sight of the Jura or the Alps to guide them, they would find it very difficult to understand the structure of Brittany or the Pays de Bray. To realize in all clarity the full persuasive strength of the transformist point of view, one should not immediately turn one's attention to any random region of the organic world. If one does, one is in danger of being impressed only by the leaps and gaps of life in movement, that is to say of perceiving only disorder. Anyone who wishes to understand the pattern of life must, before considering nature as a whole or in her most ancient strata, gradually educate his eyes, training his vision on limited and characteristic objects. And for this purpose it is essential to concentrate the attention on some animal group of particularly recent appearance and expansion, in which the links between forms are still easy to decipher.

The placental mammals,[1] whose great expansion does not seem to go back further than the (very mysterious) times that separate the Secondary from the Tertiary, are a particularly typical example of one of these recent groups. They present a clear and authentic text from which we can learn to read the lessons of life. What do we learn by observing them?

One fundamental fact, definitely established by the palaeontology of mammals, is that, in the extremely varied crowd of extinct species, it is today possible to recognize certain indubitable lines of development. We have alluded to the difficulties encountered by 'phylogenists' in their efforts to reconstruct true genealogies, that is to say series of living forms that succeed one another in time, by a gradual evolution not of a single characteristic taken in isolation but of all their characteristics together. The task has proved more difficult than was at first thought. Nevertheless the essential parts of the original work have resisted the tests of a more exacting criticism and of new discoveries. They have even grown substantially stronger. The genealogy of the horse, camel, elephant, rhinoceros, tapir,[2] dog, etc. is now fixed in its broad outlines, and allows us to go back stage by stage, from animals living today to little creatures in whom an untrained eye would look in vain for anything to remind him of the types at present living. These few solidly established lines have the same importance for zoology as the determination of a base line in surveying, or the establishment of a link in crystallography. They

---

[1] This term designates all the present-day mammals in our lands, in contrast to the non-placental or marsupial mammals, such as the kangaroos, which are today almost entirely confined to Australia.

[2] If we know the genealogy of the ungulates particularly well it is because these animals, living in great herds on the plains, are those whose remains are most often found. Ungulate fossils form at least four-fifths of the mammalian fossils that we possess.

provide in fact axes and a law of periodicity, which allows us progressively to arrange the whole confused crowd of other living
beings.

From conveniently chosen groups of ungulates and carnivores
(among others), we see beyond all doubt that there are exact, simple
and invariable rules governing the gradual and 'directed' complication of organisms. In time, one form leads to another, by way of
branches along which certain characteristics (size, complication or
simplification of teeth, modification of limbs or skull-form) grow
steadily more pronounced. Each of these branches forms a whole,
which has its own type of individuality and destiny. It is born,
develops, becomes fixed and then disappears. Hence, by examining
the characteristics of an isolated bone, we can decide without risk or
mistake, through what intermediate stages this characteristic has
passed in process of its formation. A one- or two-toed extremity, for
example, indubitably postulates the pre-existence somewhere of a
five-toed paw. The elephant's tusk is zoologically incomprehensible
without the previous existence of a state in which the second upper
incisor was small and the dentition complete, etc. etc.

Endowed by its knowledge of a few better-known groups with
the precious idea of 'oriented variation', palaeontology is thus
equipped to undertake the study of much less well represented animal
forms. Even where it so far possesses only incomplete or scattered
samples, it is nevertheless capable of tracing the broad lines of 'phyla'
or genealogical series; and the fillings-in of sometimes very large gaps
are legitimate. If we knew only one cat's skull, we could unhesitatingly affirm, by other known examples, that this animal, armed today
with only a single cutting molar in its lower jaw, presupposes
carnivores with three piercing molars (which observation confirms),
that is to say that it is in some way the successor of animals which
have absolutely no resemblance to present-day cats. This cat, presumed unique in our collections, would, alone, represent a quite certain series of successive types.

Indefatigably the palaeontology of mammals has pursued and is
still pursuing its patient labour of alignment. In long lines or short

segments, it plots an ever-increasing number of phyla or fragments of phyla on the map of life. Let us first look at the general design obtained by this process. Incomplete though it is, its significance is perfectly clear and leaps to the eye: the distribution of living forms is a phenomenon of movement and dispersion. The lines are more numerous, they intersect less often and further from us than we thought – all the same, they exist and, towards the base, they converge.

The general laws of organic development have been discovered by the examination of restricted groups. They can now be effortlessly applied to units of increasing size. Not only families and orders, but entire fauna with all the zoological elements they comprise, have moved as a whole, like simple species.

Unreflectingly, we easily imagine that all the mammals which have ever existed are of the type of our horses, dogs and elephants. Actually, the familiar group of animals of the Old World is only a feeble part of what life has produced along the mammalian line. During the Tertiary a great number of strange animals lived in Patagonia. These fantastic creatures (edentates, notungulates, etc.) are connected with the same fundamental types as our northern mammals; they have the same origins, as can be proved; only from the end of the Cretaceous onwards, they were isolated geographically, and lived their history completely apart. Similarly, in Australia and New Zealand, the varied troop of marsupials indubitably represents the result of developments undergone in isolation by a group of animals separated at a very early time (since the Jurassic, perhaps) from the great mass of placental mammals.

It is most remarkable that these weird creatures, peculiar to the southern hemisphere, by no means form a disorderly, haphazard assemblage; on the contrary, each of the two groups, proper respectively to South America and Australia, has its own structure, parallel to that of the fauna of Europe, North America and Asia. Each comprises, in its particular manner, the same fundamental morphological types. Miocene Patagonia had its solipeds, its tusked pachyderms, its pseudo-hares, its animals with trunks. Present-day Australia offers us the extraordinarily instructive spectacle of the marsupials, among which some take the place of wolves, others of the ungulates, yet others of shrews, ant-eaters, moles, etc. One might say that, to remain in equilibrium, each fauna must be supplied – as if with so many organs – with carnivores, insectivores, herbivores, etc. All this denotes movement, growth, differentiation. Taken as a single mass, the whole group of mammals manifestly obeys an *internal* law of development and irradiation. Now, vast though its proportions seem to us, it is itself, as we shall soon see, no more than a ray of another irradiation, a twig dwarfed by a much larger network of branches.

The first mammals are too ancient, too rare and too small for us to be able to state the exact circumstances of their first appearance (geology and palaeontology, as cannot be often enough repeated, only record a sequence of maxima in the movements of life and the earth's crust). On the other hand, before they entirely disappear from our eyes into the depths of time, we see the mass of them replaced in our field of vision by a new and powerful division of the vertebrates, that of the reptiles.

In the Secondary – as every schoolboy now knows – the reptiles occupied the earth. Through lack of evidence, the details of their developments are still hidden from us. But the major phases of their growth end in the gigantic and extravagant; and, more important perhaps, the manifold adjustments of their fundamental type to life on earth, in water and in the air – which are translated into an incredibly varied burgeoning of swimming, flying, herbivorous and carnivorous forms – make an astonishing spectacle of movement and plasticity. The dinosaurs alone, once considered exceptional and rare creatures, seem to have formed as powerful and varied a collection as all the mammals together. And yet they too are only a branch among many others. Far below their stratum, recent researches are beginning to discover another still more ancient expansion of life in all its breadth, that of the theromorphs – a curious compromise between the amphibians, reptiles and mammals. During the immense continental period which followed the emergence of the Carboniferous ranges, a strange population covered the earth: salamanders

supported by four massive legs in the manner of a small hippopota-
mus, dog-headed reptiles with dog's fangs or rodents' incisors, or a
skull crowned with horns like that of many herbivores. All this had
time to be born and to die. And we are still very far from the origins
of the vertebrates. Before the theromorphs were the amphibians; and
before the amphibians certainly something else which must have
been like certain fish that we still see living in what remains of the
continents of this inexpressibly distant time. At the distance they are
from us, squeezed between the Carboniferous and Permo-triassic
strata, the theromorphs and amphibians seem to have lasted only a
moment. Both must have lived, however, for as long as the dinosaurs or the mammals. Perhaps the best unit of time in geology is the
lapse necessary for the building of a mountain chain or the establishment of a universal fauna.

So, as far as the eye can see, living strata succeed one another; and
in each of them, just as in all of them together, the structure first observed in a restricted group of horses or elephants is followed as far
as the eye can see. The further we step back into the past, the more
we are reduced to noting only relationships of a superior order. But
if the law of development changes a little in its form and object – if
instead of governing the simple appearance of a characteristic in the
history of a species, it ordains the distribution of forms within whole
animal populations – basically it still remains essentially the same. In
greater and greater assemblages, living creatures replace one another,
develop and ramify according to the same rhythm. And in this
harmony the silences themselves have their precise significance.

Arguments against transformism have been found in the existence
of the huge gaps that today separate the vertebrates from the annelids, molluscs, coelenterates and, even more perhaps, the arthropods.
Examined more closely, these gaps might have appeared as what they
really are: a fresh proof of the *internal* law which governs the development of life. Let us examine the distribution of these fissures which
divide the mass of living beings in present-day nature and in our
knowledge of the past. Do they follow the play of chance? Not at all.
They follow, on the contrary, a law of perfectly clear distribution.

The sub-kingdoms which comparative anatomy has so many troubles in connecting with one another and with the vertebrates are, as is now proved, zoological stocks whose great age astounds the imagination. Before the deepest geological strata accessible to our investigations were laid down the development of these prodigiously ancient forms was already long complete. Their group should therefore seem to us particularly clear and stable. In their mass we can, of course still easily distinguish the traces of a progressive expansion analogous to that to be found in the history of the reptiles and mammals. Here and there, even on their fossilized twigs, we can still surprise rapid blossomings which testify to the liveliness of these ancient proliferations. Since primary times, the crustaceans have given birth to the decapods and *Brachyura*. The spiders have lost their segments. From the cephalopods issued the imposing legion of the ammonites. The *Lamellibranchs* themselves suddenly gave birth, in the Cretaceous, to the strange family of the rudists, bivalves that externally resemble polyparies, etc. etc. Despite everything, the zoological branches that appear when we look beyond the vertebrates are of an age absolutely distinct from that of the branch which bears us. We are the last comers, they the first born in nature. Surely there must be a gap in our knowledge corresponding to this sudden leap in generations? Lacunae exist therefore. But precisely because they punctuate and signpost the natural progress of life, they do not disturb our vision. On the contary, they help us to realize the interconnections of living beings more clearly and certainly. The mammals form so thick a clump of related species that we find it difficult to distinguish in them the great lines of evolution. Below them, where the test of time has thrown the branches into relief, the pattern simplifies and we have a wider vision. The main branches are the first to become clear. They succeed one another in depth and stand increasingly bare. At a given moment, we can no longer distinguish anything but solitary leading shoots emerging, almost without appreciable connections, from a world that has entirely disappeared. This whole mass then plunges into inaccessible depths, which will for ever hide from us the secret of life's origins. Let us not regret this darkness too much. It has its own incomparable majesty; and what it yields is enough to save us from any further doubt about the law that presided, historically, over the offshoots from the trunk on which we were born.

Truly, it is impossible to contemplate with the least informed gaze the assemblage of zoological forms as revealed to palaeontology, without being compelled to recognize that this vast edifice is not a mosaic of *artificially* grouped elements, and that the distribution of its parts is, on the contrary, the effect of a *natural* process. Even though it may be as rigid as a stone today, the great body of animal species surrounding us inevitably appears to our eyes as if in movement.[1] From the smallest detail to the hugest concentrations, *our living universe* (like our material universe) *has a structure*, and this structure can only be due to a phenomenon of growth. This is the great proof of transformism and the measure of what that theory has definitely acquired.

c *The Essence of Transformism*

Once our mind has found a fragment of order in the things around it, it cannot easily be persuaded to abandon what it has gained, but obstinately endeavours to extend and explain the law which has appeared to it in a small field. This urge to expand and interpret manifests itself very strongly in the question of transformism. No sooner do the natural sciences reveal the existence of a current of life, than we immediately want to know where the current comes from and where it is going, what cohesive force keeps its countless drops united and what mysterious slope draws its waves down.

How ought we to imagine the primordial form of life on earth? Can it have appeared as a single spore from which the great tree of species issued complete; or, on the contrary, did it perhaps condense like a great dew which quickly covered our planet with a myriad

[1] 'The longer we reflect the more clearly it appears that only the idea of a progressive development of the living world by way of evolution is capable of making the Creator's work intelligible to us.' Canon V. Grégoire, professor of Botany at Louvain University, *Revue de Questions Scientifiques*, vol. xxix, Brussels, 1921, p. 400.

initial germs in which the future plurality of living forms was already formed in advance?

Is it possible to follow through the different zoological sheets that have, one after another, spread across the world only to break up and be replaced by a younger fauna, the persistent and continuous growth of an underlying character? Is there a single direction in biological evolution, or does an objective view of things show us only an irregular proliferation of branches growing by chance. From many points of view, a radiolarian, a holothurian, a trilobite, a dinosaur are as differentiated and complicated as a primate. On the other hand, their nervous systems are much less perfect. Should we not look in this direction for the secret law of development? Should we not say that the principal stem of the zoological tree has constantly climbed in the direction of a greater and greater brain?

And now that the appearance of human intelligence, 'consciousness' has reached a maximum on earth that seems to us incapable of extension, what must we think of the future of evolution? Will life still be able to advance further with us on some new terrain, or have we perhaps reached the season when the fruit are ripe and the leaves are beginning to fall?

What is it, in fact, that has driven the world along the roads of life? By the play of what forces have we been empirically produced? To explain the present biological state of the universe, is it enough to note relationships of adaptation and selection, phenomena of mechanical harmonization and functional excitation between the organisms and the milieu that surrounds us. Or must we, on the other hand, shift the true dynamism of evolution to a psychological centre of vital expansion and understand it as a positive urge towards the light?

All these questions arise when we begin to see the face of life as a whole. They are legitimate and exciting. Nevertheless the problems they put are logically of secondary importance; any solutions found for them leave intact the question of transformism itself. This is the point that must be precisely understood.

What makes a transformist is not, let it be clearly stated, that he is a Darwinist or Lamarckian, a mechanist or vitalist, a mono- or polyphyletist. It is not even the belief (paradoxical though this may seem) that living beings descend from one another by generation, properly so called. Those who know nature are sufficiently convinced of its power and secrets to admit that special organic phenomena – never yet observed by human eye – may once have presided over the birth of zoological types and the multiplication of species. This hypothesis is not very probable, but it still remains possible. In any case, it is not this that would disturb the transformists. What modern natural scientists most fundamentally hold to – what they cling to as an unshakeable conviction, a conviction that has continuously grown beneath their surface arguments – is the fact of a *physical connection* between living beings. 'Living beings *hold together* biologically. They have organic command of their successive appearances, so that neither man, the horse nor the first cell could have appeared earlier or later than they did. As a consequence of this observable connection between living forms we must look for, and may find, a material basis, that is to say a scientific reason, for their links with one another. The successive growths of life may be the *substance of a history* 'This is the sufficient' and necessary 'faith' that makes a transformist. All the rest is argument between systems, or even alien passions, wrongly confused with a question of a purely scientific order. Reduced to this final essence, understood as a simple belief in the existence of a physical connection, founded on experience, between living beings (a connection whose nature is still undetermined), transformism looks extremely harmless and extremely strong. It could not cause offence to any philosophy and, furthermore, it occupies a seemingly impregnable position. This I shall now prove.

For transformism to be dangerous to reason and faith, it would have to claim that the action of a Creator fills no purpose, to reduce the development of life to a process purely immanent in nature, to state that 'the greater can automatically arise from the less.' Too many evolutionists have, in fact, committed this serious mistake of taking their scientific explanation of life for a metaphysical solution of the world. Like the materialistic biologist who thinks he is abolishing the soul when he analyses the physico-chemical mechanisms of the living cell, zoologists have imagined that they have rendered the primal cause useless because they were discovering a little more clearly the general structure of its work. It is time definitely to shelve a theorem so badly stated. No, scientific transformism, strictly speaking, proves nothing for or against God. It simply notes the fact of a chain of connection in reality. It presents us with an anatomy of life, certainly not a final reason for it. It affirms that 'something organized itself, something grew.' But it is incapable of discerning the ultimate conditions of that growth. To decide whether the movement of evolution is intelligible in itself, or if it requires a progressive and continuous creation implemented by a prime mover, this is a question that depends on metaphysics.

Transformism, we must tirelessly repeat, imposes no philosophy. Does this mean that it does not hint at one? Of course not. But here, strangely enough, we notice that the systems of thought which suit it best are, perhaps, precisely those which thought themselves the most threatened. Christianity, for example, is essentially founded on the double belief that man is an object specially pursued by the divine power throughout creation, and that Christ is the end supernaturally but physically marked out as the consummation of humanity. Could one ask for an empirical view of things in closer accordance with these statements of unity than this, in which we discover living beings not artificially juxtaposed with the dubious aim of utility or ornament, but bound together by virtue of physical conditions in the reality of a conjoint effort towards greater being?

But disregarding these harmonies and their attraction, a more brutal necessity obliges us willy-nilly to take into account the 'generalized' transformism of which we have just stated the essence. No scientific explanation of the world seems capable of taking the place that it occupies.

It is quite easy to criticize transformism. Why is it so difficult to find a solution that will enable us to dispense with it? The problem of the distribution of living beings in nature is one that faces everybody. One must therefore look for an answer. We require it not for a reprehensible whim or for the pleasure of argument, but because we

23

are impelled by all that is most sacred in man: the need to know and to orient himself.

Only one logical method of explaining the unity and interconnection of life is available to the non-transformist: that is to admit an *ideal* connection of forms. This is to maintain that the law of succession of living beings is entirely concentrated in a creative thought which develops at successive points, successively placed, the design that it has in its wisdom conceived. By this hypothesis, living forms would call one another into existence solely by virtue of a logical series of relays existing in the divine thought. These would be points cosmically independent of one another in their origins, but harmoniously disseminated on a sheaf of imaginary curves.

This solution seems incapable of acceptance by any natural scientist; and for two reasons:

Firstly, it is in practice inapplicable, since were it operative it would multiply the number of independent creations to an infinite figure. Why not accept a special creation for those two kinds of wasps and sorrel that you declare by virtue of your experiments completely fixed, if you want one for the origin of rodents or perissodactyls? And if you say that slight variations may have been possible, what limit would you put on the extent of these variations accumulating for long periods of time?

But this is not all. Even if the 'fixed-type' school were to succeed in defining in a non-arbitrary fashion the number and place of the creative severances (even if they were to postulate only a single severance!) they would strike a fundamental difficulty: that our mind finds it impossible to conceive any absolute beginning in the order of phenomena. Try to imagine the abrupt appearance in nature of a being which was not 'born' from a number of pre-existing physical circumstances. What would it be like? If you have ever studied a real object, you will renounce an attempt of which you are bound to see the vanity. Every being in our universe is by its material organization part and parcel of a whole past. It is in essence a history. And by its history, by this chain of antecedents which have prepared and introduced it, it is joined with no severance to the milieu within which it appears to us. The smallest exception to this rule would upset the entire edifice of our experience.

People go on repeating that 'transformism is a hypothesis'. The statement is true when we are discussing theories held by a disciple of Lamarck or Darwin. But if we want it to mean that we are free to regard or not to regard living beings as a sequence of elements which have appeared 'in the physical function' one from another (whatever the exact nature of this function may be), then we are deceiving ourselves. *Reduced to its essence*, transformism is not a hypothesis. It is the particular expression, applied to the case of life, of the law which conditions our whole knowledge of the sensible universe: the law that we can understand nothing, in the domain of matter, except as part of a sequence or collection.

Translated into creationist language, this law is perfectly simple and orthodox. It means that when the primal cause operates, it does not insert itself among the elements of this world but acts directly on their natures, so that God, as one might say, does not so much 'make' things as 'make them make themselves'.

What must appear astonishing, therefore, is not that believers are rallying to the truth that underlies transformism, but rather that they do not recognize more easily beneath the sometimes unacceptable language of the evolutionists the Catholic and traditional tendency to defend the value of second causes. A very well-informed theologian who is also a true scholar recently went so far as to call this tendency by the fine name of 'Christian naturalism'.[1]

Etudes, 5–20 June 1921.

[1] The spirit of Christian naturalism has always been honoured by the Church; and only in times of decadence has it been seen to some extent to weaken. What I mean by *Christian naturalism* is the tendency to attribute to the natural action of secondary causes everything that reason and the positive findings of the observational sciences do not forbid them to, and only to invoke a special intervention of God, distinct from the actions of his general governance, in case of absolute necessity.' Henri de Dorlodot, Professor of geology in the University of Louvain, formerly professor of Theology in the Seminary of Namur *Le Darwinisme au point de vue de l'orthodoxie catholique*, Louvain, 1913, p. 93. New edition, Brussels, Vromant, 1921, p. 115.

CHAPTER II

THE FACE OF THE EARTH

The title at the head of these pages is that of the Austrian geologist Suess's book in which he drew the portrait of our planet, the general relief of which he came to understand by a marvellous effort of synthesis. My reasons for using these words 'The Face of the Earth' is that they admirably express and resume the results reached by geological science in the last half-century. The earth has a physiognomy, a countenance, a face.

In the past men were capable of imagining that the earth which bore them stretched around them horizontally farther than the eye could see, or that it ended abruptly in the marvellous lands of Elysium or hell. For our fathers, the world was so clearly an indefinitely flat surface that it took them centuries of reflection and dangerous voyages to break the spell of appearances and make the mental circuit of the globe. Today, a new effort to improve our perspectives is just coming to a head. Having made the circuit of our universe, we are just beginning to decipher its features. Patiently assembled, the innumerable details gathered about the earth's surface are beginning to fit together. They are gaining meaning for our eyes. Soon it will be no more permissible for an educated man to be ignorant that the earth has a face, an expression, than not to know that it is round and revolves.

Let us try to see this noble and venerable visage in its chief outlines. And for that purpose, let us ask what aspect the mountains, continents and oceans have assumed for modern science.[1]

---

[1] If Father Teilhard de Chardin had revised this article for publication, he would no doubt have indicated in notes the most recent progress made by geologists in their researches on the origins of mountains and continents. Being unable to make good this deficiency, we have confined ourselves to a few indications. – Editor of Collected Edition.

I. THE MOUNTAINS

A *Geological Character of the Mountains*

Everybody in our age has seen mountains. Everybody, at least once in his life, has wanted to enjoy their picturesqueness or their bleakness. But among the crowds who visit these most spectacular parts of our country every year, how many bring back from their expeditions anything but the memory of beautiful slopes and abrupt crests, covered with pines or carpeted with heather? How many wanderers in the Vosges, the Alps or the Pyrenees have suspected the true secret hidden in these exceptional places? For truly informed people, mountainous parts of the globe take on a far more extraordinary aspect. They assume quite a different personality than for simple tourists. From the geologist's point of view, not only the external relief of the mountains is wonderful, but their substance, their very stuff is peculiar, so peculiar that often one has only to present them with a small bit of it, picked up far away, and they will say immediately, without hesitation: 'That stone has been broken off from a mountain.' What then characterizes the matter of which mountains are made?

Four things principally: the marine character of the sediments, the hardening of which has formed the rocky beds; the astonishing thickness of these petrified deposits; the frequent transformation of the originally muddy mass into true crystallized rocks; lastly the folding, and often the unimaginable crushing in the final steps undergone by this enormous accumulation of stones.

These four characteristics of the mountain beds are not hard to grasp. One simple example will help us to understand and remember them.

Let us transport ourselves, in thought, to one of those quarries outside Paris from which gypsum is dug, to Argenteuil for example or Romainville. If we visit these quarries, we shall notice, on a thickness of about 50 metres, a series of perfectly horizontal beds alternately of hard gypsum and soft green or blue clays. Informed by the fossils to be found both in the gypsum and the clays, geologists place these rocks in the formation which they call the upper Eocene; they recognize in them the barely altered bottom of a saline lagoon, on the banks of which lived a herbivorous population belonging to zoological forms that have long ago disappeared. Let us suppose now that we travel away from Paris to the south-east, and that we can trace, stage by stage as far as the Alps, the bed of sediments deposited on France at the same epoch as the plaster of Paris stone, this result has been attained by indirect means. We should notice, as we drew nearer to the Alps, a singular modification in the aspect of the deposits. At first the geological beds become thicker, and their nature changes. No more remains of land mammals or fresh water shells: but only of marine molluscs, and soon, nothing but the shells of very small *Foraminifera* scattered over an ocean of hardened mud. Let us advance further towards the central zone of the Alps; and it is extremely difficult to observe even these humble fossils. Where the thickness of the beds becomes greatest, in fact (hundreds of metres), the rock assumes another texture; gradually from clayey it becomes crystalline, sometimes as crystalline as granite. And then it falls into folds: the beds become laminated, crumpled, crushed. Organic remains have generally quite disappeared in this wild confusion of stone. Although the detail is chaotic, the general structure (the overall form) of the beds is not disorderly: the building up of geological maps has revealed in the Alps many folds lying one above the other and sometimes lying in such a way that, prised loose from their base, they may easily have slid or been carried one above another for a distance that may be as great as 100 kilometres.[1]

The experiment that we have imagined taking place between Paris and the great Alpine ranges might be repeated for all terrains and all mountains. The result of these repeated observations would be the same. Always in going from the plains to the mountains, we observe that first the geological sediments become thicker, and then their inner structure alters, whilst at the same time their general

[1] The author would probably have revised this figure.

28

architecture is disrupted.[1] By all appearances these very special formations have a reason for their existence. Attempts have been made to explain them by the hypothesis of 'geosynclinals'.

A geosyncline, for modern geology, is a region of the earth in which, first, the earth's crust (lithosphere) is thinner than elsewhere, and where, secondly, sedimentation takes place with particular rapidity. Let us imagine such a region in some part of the world. Under the continuously growing weight of sediments, the lithosphere, by hypothesis relatively supple, gives way, falls in, forms a pocket. The bottom of the pocket, going down to zones where the temperature and pressure are greater, where the action also of certain solvents is particularly strong, undergoes a transformation, a recrystallization, a 'metamorphosization', of the muddy material it contains. This is the story of a geosynclinal during its filling-up phase, that is to say in the 'gestation' period of the mountains. Now (probably as a result of the contraction of the globe) there comes a lateral stress which squeezes (and no doubt at the same time a vertical stress that raises) the mass of the slowly accumulated deposits: the pocket will be compressed; its contents will fold inside in all directions and will tend to rise to the surface in the form of a bolster. The mountain is now being born.

We are already beginning to understand how special and complicated is the phenomenon called 'orogenesis'. A mountain cannot tower up at any time and anywhere on the surface of the earth. A mountain is the result of a process, lasting countless centuries, first of sedimentation, then of exteriorization. It can only arise at chosen places after an interminable maturing.

B *Geographical Distribution of Mountain Chains*

Since 'mountainous terrains' are not uniformly spread over our globe, it has been thought interesting to follow and understand their distribution across our present continents. Because of the immense extent of mountain regions, and the need to distinguish between

[1] This is especially true of the Alps, the Pyrenees and the Jura.

ranges of different ages, this task of plotting was both extremely laborious and extremely delicate. It has nevertheless been carried through; and the result of these geographical and geological explorations has been the discovery that the geosynclinals are distributed on a determined plan around our planet. In this way the facial features of the earth have begun to be distinguishable to us.

Let us consider first of all the mountains which are best known to us, because most recently formed: the Alps and the Tertiary ranges contemporary with them. Deceived by geographical names, we sometimes imagine that the Alps do not extend beyond Switzerland or the countries bordering on Switzerland. Geology recognizes the Alpine formations as a power of an altogether different kind. If we consider the dynamic unity of the movement that threw them up, or analyse the stratigraphical character of the beds composing them, the 'great Alps' form an unbroken ring round the earth.[1] To the west, we see them forming the backbone of the Italian peninsula, the northern crests of the Atlas, the Pyrenees, then, sinking beneath the waters of the Atlantic, to reappear in the region of the West Indies. Towards the east, their folds form the Carpathians, a part of the Balkans and the Caucasus. They cross Cilicia as the Taurus, then to Iran. Farther on, they are called the Himalayas. Then they reach the Sunda Islands. There they suddenly change form. Hitherto strongly concentrated and forming a roughly equatorial girdle, their line now breaks into two, and forms a wide circle almost a meridian, right round the Pacific, by way of New Guinea, New Zealand, Japan and the Aleutians, and the American cordilleras, north and south, joined, on the level of Mexico, to the line of mountains that we last noticed in the neighbourhood of the West Indies. Let us put this

[1] We are speaking here, as the quotation marks indicate, of the Alpine chain in its broad sense, 'for, so far as the Alps proper are concerned, the truly Alpine movements go back to the Liassic. In America the movements which folded the Andine cordilleras (Andine movements) date from the end of the Jurassic, and had a phase of Alpine paroxysm towards the end of the Cretaceous. Lastly, in the Pyrenees, the first phase of folding dates from the middle Cretaceous'. *Précis de géologie.* L. Moret. (publ. Masson) – Ed.

were caught and folded in the very centre of the Tertiary chains. Our Alps therefore had not yet started to move, and already a plain, soon followed by the sea,[1] stretched in the place of the Carboniferous mountains. Let us add, therefore, to the whole age occupied by the building of the Alpine system the time needed for those glorious crests to be brought (by erosion and continental subsidences) to sea level, and we shall get an idea how many centuries are represented by the second and smaller half of Primary times. The extent of this cycle astounds us. We must add to it an equal quantity of time if we want to step yet further back in the history of the earth.

When, on the site of the Carboniferous chain, levelled before the rise of the Alps, there still stretched a deep sea, and still farther north, bordering that sea, a third chain of mountains, as old[2] compared with the Carboniferous Alps, as they are compared with our Tertiary, the Silurian Alps or Caledonian chain had already entirely broken up. Who then would be bold enough to measure in figures the abyss of time that has passed away? Here, once more to designate the immense time needed for the construction and destruction of these folds, whose mesh must have enveloped the earth, we have only two short geological periods: The Cambrian and Silurian. But this, as we feel, is merely the effect of distance. The beginnings of Primary times, with their thousands of metres of uniform sediments, perhaps represent as many years as have passed since we suppose them to have ended. On account of its vast antiquity the Silurian chain is more difficult to trace than the Hercynian. We recognize it, however, very distinctly in a long zone that runs through Newfoundland, Scotland, Scandinavia, Spitzbergen and the north of Greenland. In Norway its peaks appear to challenge those of much more recent mountains; but their altitude is exceptional. It is due to a late raising up of the continental platform in which its roots are sunk.

Have we now finished with the waves of stone which ceaselessly

[1] To be more explicit: beaten by the sea which gradually covered its surface. – Ed.

[2] In fact still older. It is the oldest that can be dated by fossils; by recent computations, it would already have been four hundred million years old. – Ed.

rise before us, each time we try to advance a little further into the past and towards the north? No, not yet. On the northern edge of the sea, in which the Caledonian chains were being prepared, in the Cambrian, there were already mountains of which we find the really affecting traces in Canada, the Hebrides, the west of Norway: the Huronian chain, the pre-Cambrian Alps. The study of these Alps is extremely difficult, not only because their relief has entirely disappeared but because their roots have furthermore been abraded almost to the base. No fossils to date their beds, and only just enough indications for us to be sure that we are dealing with ancient folded sediments. Indeed, the Huronian chain is the last of which present-day geology can attempt to trace the outlines. But it is not on that account the last of which we detect the existence. If we study very closely the rocky material of which the pre-Cambrian mountains are made, we notice that this material has been several times folded and abraded before being used to form these last crests. There, where stood the most ancient chain that we can define, there were geosynclinals, then mountains, then geosynclinals again! In the course of geological time, we can distinguish only four mountainous waves descending from the pole towards the equator. But we are sure that before that series of folds other indecipherable quiverings ran across the face of the earth. For the geologist looking into the past, there is no last chain in sight.

Let us leave these vague perspectives, so important for our right vision of reality, but so fugitive when examined by our science, to return to our observation of the four great chains: the Alpine, the Hercynian, the Caledonian and Huronian, the outlines of which are approximately known to us. We have not yet fully penetrated their character. To understand properly indeed the place which these four huge and more or less concentric masses occupy on the face of our globe, we must recognize that they represent so many zones of advance of the earth's crust consolidated on the moving band of the geosynclinals. And this leads us to study the continental regions or areas.

II. *THE CONTINENTS*

So far, being completely occupied with the origin of the mountains, we have kept our eyes firmly fixed on the sea-bottoms from which the folds of the earth's crust emerged one by one; and by following the movement backwards into the past, we have been able to see the Mesogean, relatively narrow in the Tertiary, spreading immeasurably in pre-Cambrian times. To observe the birth of the continents (at least in our hemisphere) it will be enough for us to follow the phenomenon in the reverse direction, that is to say to return to the present by observing this time not the southern, marine face of the folds in progress, but their northern face, which has so far been hidden from us.

Let us take the movement at its beginnings (for us); in other words, let us take our place at the time when, at the mean latitude of the Hebrides, the great transverse sea was beating the buttresses of the last of the pre-Cambrian chains. What should we have found as we travelled northwards from this shore? A large solidified expanse. Behind the Huronian peaks – we have proof of this – was a sheltered and raised region, probably a tableland in relief, built on several stages of abraded mountains, but definitely unfitted to fold. A sort of rocky shield covered the north of Canada, and stretched across the present-day Atlantic as far as the Lofoten Islands. Other similar shields occupied the place of Finland and northern Siberia. Let us look carefully at these pieces of carapace scarcely raised above the waters. We do not know what sort of life – or indeed if any life – rejoiced their soil, countless times swept since the Primary by all sorts of ice and floods. But we know that their surfaces, gradually collected and added to, finally created the good firm earth that supports and nourishes our civilization.

The first rough sketches of the continents we perceive formed disconnected elements, therefore, lying almost entirely in the north. It was left for the successive foldings of the earth's crust to cement the pieces and extend the borders of this narrow domain. First, the construction and destruction of the Caledonian chain stretched a long band of ferruginous sandstone in front of the Huronian platform. Then came the turn of the Hercynian chain which traced, in front of this red band, the thick black halo of its coal lands. Finally, the Alpine chains, dismissing into the distance what remained of the Mesogean, mark the last zones to be conquered from the waters of a circle of snow.

Thus, from some primitive fragments a vast North Atlantic territory took shape as large as Europe, Asia and North America together – a land often partially invaded by shallow seas, and (as we shall state in a moment) capable of breaking but incapable of giving birth to new mountains. In terms of geology a continent is not principally land that has risen up. It is land that has become stiff, and to which only one kind of movement, other than breaking, is henceforth possible: a slow alternate movement of sinking and rising as a mass. It is as if the earth were breathing – unless the age-long oscillations of the shores, which we have noticed with surprise, are merely a repercussion of invisible tremors troubling the inaccessible bottom of the great waters.

However, at the same time as the northern continent was gradually bringing its beaches down to the latitudes of our Mediterranean, seemingly another great land was rising out of the southern deeps to meet it. The history of the ranges lying south of the Mesogean is still, at least for the earliest epochs, very obscure. Some indications, however, lead us to believe that several waves of the lithosphere, symmetrical with those coming from the north, arose successively in the south, enlarging the continental surfaces a little each time, and equally reducing the areas of sea. One suspects a Caledonian chain across the Sahara. A Hercynian chain certainly plays a part in the construction of the southern Atlas. Lastly, the Alps visibly extend along the Algerian littoral. In the space encircled by these various successive folds, that is to say placed symmetrically to the North Atlantic continent in relation to the Mesogean, there existed for a long time a truly enormous land, Gondwanaland (as Suess calls it), whose sandstone tablelands and special fossils (surviving in our day in the lung-fish of Queensland, central Africa and Brazil) are found across the entire surface of South America, Africa, Madagascar, India and Australia.[1]

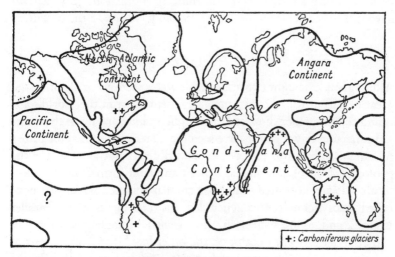

Uralo-Permian palaeogeography. (R. Furon.)

Must we suppose, with certain great geologists, that a third great continent, also formed of additive annular chains, occupied until a relatively recent date the enormous surface covered by the Pacific. If so, we have three shields, each one about as big as a third of the earth's surface, which would have come into contact, towards the end of the Tertiary, as a result of the emersion of the Alpine geosynclinal:

[1] On November 8, 1951, Father Teilhard de Chardin wrote from Buenos Aires: 'Lastly, it will have been very useful to me to have visited Argentina immediately after leaving South Africa, for it has given me a sharp impression (both from the geological and anthropological point of view) of the similarities and contrasts between the two continents. It was with a shock that I discovered here a Permian glaciation and Devonian sandstones like those I had just left in Durban and the Cape (a point for Wegener . . .), and as for Man, there is another shock: just after leaving the centre of the 'explosion' of the palaeolithic industry (in Africa), to find here the wave at the end of its journey, that is to say at its extreme point of expansion, after crossing the full extent of Asia and the whole length of America . . .'

indeed the sea would have disappeared, *if* the effect of the growth of continents by the action of folding had not been counterbalanced (and more) by a sudden and disturbing phenomenon, of which we have still to speak: the subsidences, which gave rise to the oceans.

III. *THE OCEANS*

Although at first sight expanses of salt water seem to us all alike, the great oceans of today constitute an element apart in the world's appearance, altogether distinct in its origin and history from the zones of immersion in which we have seen the materials destined for future mountains piling up. Just as one land differs from another for the geologist (land of continental deposit and land formed by folding), so all seas are not alike. The vast circular channels which we have called geosynclinals once encircled the continents with annular troughs, and, as we have seen, these trenches disappeared by filling and contraction. The oceans, on the other hand, form large areas of depression, in which the sedimentation may be practically nil: and since the beginnings of geological time, their domain seems to have been growing continuously. The geosynclinals are abysses which emerge. What the oceans have gained, on the other hand, their depths retain. This is what renders their nature puzzling and leaves the geologist the right to remain strangely thoughtful while he stands on the sea-shore, and watches this huge, deep and liquid mass rising and falling around the earth which bears humanity and its fortunes.

Let us briefly follow the establishment of the oceans' reign on the surface of the earth.

At the end of the Carboniferous age, the sea seems to have been entirely concentrated in the two great Mediterranean and circum-Pacific channels. With the exception of the Arctic Ocean (which seems always to have existed) and the geosynclines we see nothing but land everywhere: the Pacific land (perhaps); the North Atlantic continent, certainly, stretching from China to the Rockies right across Europe; and then, filling the southern hemisphere, the immensities of Gondwanaland. Let us take a quick glance at these majestic expanses, such as the face of the earth will doubtless never know again. They are too great to last; and half geology since the Secondary era is no more than the history of their fractures.

The largest was the most fragile. The southern continent was the first to fissure. First a wide crevice, still visible as the Mozambique channel, separated the Indo–Madagascan block from Africa and Brazil (which were still united). This division (as old as the end of the Triassic) was succeeded by several others in the course of the Secondary: towards the end of the Cretaceous, India was split from Madagascar, and Australia was cut off for ever from the other continents. imprisoning a fauna unique in its kind in its territory. Science finds in this fauna one of the most dazzling evidences presented by nature in favour of the gradual variations of life. Thus what we call the Indian Ocean was dug in the heart of the continental lands. The Atlantic Ocean seems to be considerably more recent. At its beginnings (at the beginning of the Tertiary) we seem to see it advancing slowly from the south like a long arm of sea, between Africa and Brazil. But this is no more than a suspicion, founded principally on zoological considerations. Soon we have no more doubt. The waters make large advances northwards. They cross the Mediterranean line, which the Indian crevasses had respected on the other side of Africa. At the end of the Tertiary, though we do not actually know when or how, the fine North Atlantic link was definitely broken; and as fragments of its ancient unity there now remain only stubs of the Hercynian and Alpine ranges which, like the piers of a bridge that has sunk into the water, face one another from shore to shore of the Old and New World. The Pacific Continent (if it really existed) has vanished like a ship of which no wreckage survives to tell its fate – lost at sea.

How do firm lands collapse to give birth to oceans? We now understand: by fractures and subsidences.

The continents, as we have seen, are a stiff shield, incapable of bending. But they may break, like the ice-sheet on a frozen pond. And they have so certainly broken, indeed, that the various effects of their fractures are everywhere visible to our eyes in their accompanying volcanoes and lava-fields. Sometimes on the surface of the continents themselves, the earth is crossed by a system of parallel cracks, which determine the formation of long compartments, prone to sink into one another: such are the Limagne of Auvergne and the Rhine trench. Sometimes the fractures intersect, constructing a chess-board of which the squares, forming sharp angles, are liable to become raised in such a way as to form polygonal piles (or horsts) such are the Vosges or the central plateau (of France). Lastly, sometimes there are no straight faults; but certain regions, encircled by a folded chain, come in a sense unstuck and collapse in the middle of their mountain enclosure. The Hungarian plain, surrounded by the Carpathians is an example of one of these 'almond-shaped' sinkings. Let us now turn to look at the oceans. We notice immediately that they are bounded by the same sort of fractures. The Red Sea, prolonged southwards by the depression in which the great African lakes are aligned, immense though it may be, is a trough. Greenland, the Crimea, Sinai, India, South Africa and many other triangular peninsulas are horsts. The Mediterranean is merely a series of sunken kernels still surrounded by mountains. And the whole Pacific itself is strangely like a gigantic almond.

One could truthfully say that today, after the age of undulations and overthrusts, the era of sinkings has begun on the face of the earth. The destructive effects of the breaking of continents, all round us, seem more important and fresher than the effects of folding, which built the mountains. If it seemed possible for a moment to believe in the total emersion of the sea-depths, we now see that a day will come, on the other hand, when a universal sea will stretch over the face of the earth.

We have now reached the end of our examination. Oceans, continents, mountains. Have not these monotonous features of our globe, these brown or blue hatchings or expanses, that we have looked at with boredom in our atlases since childhood, begun to assume for us a sort of life and shape? How can we express, in conclusion, the appearance which their face now takes in our eyes?

It must certainly be confessed that we are not entirely satisfied with the picture of our planet in so far as we have at present deciphered its features. First, there are the gaps in our knowledge. In large regions (Central Asia and New Guinea, for example), the structure of the earth's crust is still unknown to us; and these blanks are annoying. But, more serious still, the description of our world in its particular details is unsatisfactory. We should like to know if the system of folds, compartments, and breaks which geology has discovered represents accidental features, 'individual' to this earth, or if, on the contrary, it reveals a general law of solidification, of 'crystallization'[1] in all the planets. Many attempts have been made to reduce the geometrical appearance presented by our world to a simple form (the tetrahedron or another), but always in vain. Shall we therefore never succeed in making the face of the earth not merely clear to our eyes but intelligible in our minds?

Let us not despair. Geology is far from having said its last word. Not only will rapidly growing opportunities for travel hasten the exploration of the surface layers of the world, but new methods of investigation are being prepared, which will allow us to explore the secret life also of the planet that bears us. Already the analysis of the earth's vibrations (the earth vibrates indeed, like a gong, with each earthquake) is beginning to give us an idea of the distribution of densities and rigidities beneath the stony crust dissected by geologists. Soon, it is to be hoped, by means of a close network of geodesical points (established with absolute precision, thanks to the instantaneous transmission of time by wireless) the geometrical form of the globe will be so exactly ascertained at each moment that it will be possible to discover, not only the precise shape of the terrestrial geoid, but even the variations in that shape : then we shall be aware of the stretchings, contractions and spasms of all kinds that probably affect, for a variety of reasons, the drop of still molten matter which carries us on its way. When our measurements reach this perfection we shall certainly understand much better what factors influenced and what laws governed the successive formation and destruction

---

[1] It is clear that by reverting to this metaphor, the author did not intend to assimilate geological phenomena to those of crystallization. – Ed.

of the fundamental features of geographical relief. After patiently reconstructing, step by step, the broad outlines of the world, we shall at last be capable (such is the aim of every science) of deducing from a few simple data, the actual form of the earth.

But why, some may ask, undertake this labour? What is the pleasure in getting a better view of the face of this enormous and tiresome ball on the surface of which we are imprisoned? What is it that bends man irremediably to the useless task of understanding the earth?

The answer is easy. What has sustained the efforts of thousands of geologists and explorers, particularly in the last century – what sent Commander Shackleton, only a few months ago, to the desolate ice-floes of the Antarctic, with a whole people applauding him – is the sacred need to know.

Persistently, driven by a secret instinct and taught by long experience, man believes that no scrap of truth is sterile, that the smallest scientific discovery is an irreplaceable element, without which the entire waking of his consciousness, that is to say the completion of his soul, will not take place. Earth is bound to him like a monstrous problem. He has thrown himself upon it. Who would dare to say that he has not emerged greater from this contact with the unknown?

To have achieved the mastery of the earth's present and past form, as we have it today, is a fourfold and magnificent victory over those crushing, materializing realities which we call size and duration, the false constants, the dispersion of things and energies.

Victory over size, firstly, because, microscopic beings though we are, confined by a horizon of a few kilometres, we have succeeded in surmounting the almost infinite extent of matter which crushes us by its proximity, and synthesizing in a point of our minds the interminable lengths of the mountains, the dispiriting expanses of the seas and continents.

Victory over duration next, because imprisoned by nature in an almost instantaneous section of time we have succeeded in our efforts to take the plans of the past from their hiding-place and hold them before our eyes, separating them from one another in a satisfactory perspective. Let us remember the Tertiary ranges already in ruins in the Pyrenees when they are still stirring in the Andes or Alaska. Let us remember the stone waves rising interminably from the depths of the past: the Carboniferous before the Tertiary Alps; the Silurian Alps before the Carboniferous, the Huronian Alps before the Silurian; and, last of all, before the Huronian Alps, the whole series of anonymous ranges, so worn that each of them forms no more, so to speak, than a geological layer in the foundations of the oldest continents.

Victory over the false constants too, that is to say over the simplicity which makes us believe that all things have always been as we have seen them for so long as humanity remembers. Let us think of the continents which once stretched across the Atlantic from Siberia to Canada, from Australia to Brazil. Let us think of the deep swell on the site of the Alps and Himalayas. When we reflect on these things does not our mind open on perspectives of quite other changes?

Victory over dispersion, last of all. And this is the last triumph which contains all the rest, because it is a kind of creation. Just as in the life of a self-disciplined man of conscience, the originally disconnected elements of the hereditary passions and the acquired qualities end by combining in an original personality, which is the true man; so the disjointed features of terrestrial topography have by our efforts acquired a sort of single appearance. Where at first glance we saw only an incoherent distribution of altitudes, lands and waters, we have succeeded in putting together a solid network of true relationships. We have given life to the earth by lending it some of our unity.

And now, by a fruitful reverse effect, this life which our intelligence has infused in the greatest material mass that has been placed in our reach, tends to rise again in us in a new form. Having given its 'personality' to the iron and stone earth before our eyes, we have come to feel a contagious desire to construct, in our turn, from the sum total of our souls, a spiritual edifice as vast as that on which we gaze; as vast as the earth that was born from the labour of geogenical forces. All around the rocky sphere whose physical vicissitudes he described with such mastery, Suess, whose name we recalled at the beginning, saw the biosphere stretching like a veritable stratum of animated matter, the stratum of living beings and humanity. The great educative value of geology is that by revealing to us a truly *unified* earth, an earth that, having one face, has only one body, it reminds us of the organizational possibilities even more deeply concealed in the zone of thought that envelops the world. Indeed it is impossible habitually to keep one's eyes on the great horizons discovered by science without an obscure desire arising to see a growing knowledge and sympathy so linking men that, as a result of some divine attraction, there shall be only one heart and one soul on the face of the earth.[1]

The following fragments taken from letters addressed by P. Teilhard de Chardin to the eminent zoologist H. Termier, indicate the more recent attitudes of the author of this article:

Jan. 25, 1953. Fundamentally, you hold to the idea of geological movements purely repetitive in type – not additive. In other words, you hold that outside life, which evolves additively, all remains constant, 'actual', in the up-and-down play of sedimentation.

Now is this quite certain?

For my part, I cannot escape the evidence (or at least the suspicion) that beneath the pulsing rhythm of trangressions and regressions, a certain number of 'tides' or fundamental drifts take place. Slow and continuous evolutions in the composition of the atmosphere and hydrosphere, perhaps. But above all, the gradual and irreversible expansion and raising up of the continents (by granitization of the lithosphere?)

From this point of view the geological study of the biosphere would no longer be simply an analysis of animal and vegetable speciation in relation to a uniform oscillation of the geographical contours of the Earth. The true problem would become this: how to detect and define the relationships (or non-relationships) between *two* evolutions taking place simultaneously in the course of geological

[1] *Études*, December 5-20, 1921.

times. 'Evolution of the continents' and 'biogenesis' or, what comes to the same thing, in more precise terms:
'Continentalization' and 'speciation' (or 'cerebration').

March 17, 1954. What would be interesting for you petrologists would be to discover that beneath the successive waves of events, is hidden a tide (drift) expressing (despite the phenomenon of the repetition of magmas at distances of several million years) some continuous chemical change in the lithosphere. Owing to the thickening of the continents, the extrusions of 'Plutonian' no doubt take place more rarely or less copiously. But could there not be, in addition, in time some gradual modification of the Plutonian itself?

In the matter of megatectonics, I will say to you only:

(1) That I do not much believe in the sinkings of continents;

(2) And that I have a certain distrust of the importance given to geosynclinals. Not that I deny their existence – only that I wonder whether they are not given a sort of absolute and definitively localized value which they perhaps do not possess. Instinctively (from what I have been able to see) 'geosynclines' are simply *joints* (of all orders of magnitude) forming (and 'petrogenizing') either between continents, or between fragments of continents. Instinctively, therefore, I should prefer to the geology of marine transgressions and geosynclines (both so dear to the great Haug who has influenced us all) a geology based and centred on the genesis of the continents.

Nov. 11, 1954. I have in front of me your book (*Formation des Continents et Progression de la Vie*). What pleases me most in your attempted synthesis is the fundamental thesis that there is a gradual genesis of the sial – and that the continents are no more than the sum of the various kernels (accumulating peripherically and gradually welded together) in this progressive silification of the lithosphere.

I wonder more and more whether the Quaternary glaciation was not, at least in its intensity, a phenomenon of an absolutely new type in the earth's history: precisely connected with the critical stage reached by planetary continentalization at the end of the Tertiary.

From this point of view the 'Gondwanian' and Pre-Cambrian permo-carboniferous glaciations must be interpreted as due to 'premonitory' bursts of continentalization; but they would be far from having the intensity (or the character of an 'established régime') of the Quaternary glaciations. And there would not actually have been any glacial periods between the Permian and the Quaternary (of course not believing in the Drift, but in the Expansion of Continents, I could not take seriously the idea of the migration of ice-caps, once accepted by Grabau – and quite recently, I believe, revived by K. M. Creer of Cambridge, who bases himself on the residual magnetism of the rocks). These rather 'wild' reflections, as they say in English, will show you how much your pages have 'stimulated' me.

Go on reminding geologists that, in all prudence, after so much analysis, the moment has perhaps come for synthesizing. We were so busy counting the waves that we were beginning to forget the tide. You have warned us against this. And you are right.

CHAPTER III

ON THE LAW OF IRREVERSIBILITY IN EVOLUTION

This law is not special to palaeontology, but is constantly assumed or verified in all the sciences which deal with physical realities (sociology, linguistics, natural science). It applies everywhere where there is heredity. Since, in fact, a being stores traces of each phase that it goes through, it is incapable, by construction, of returning exactly to any of the states through which it has passed.

Theoretically therefore the existence of the law of irreversibility seems indisputable. In practice, its application is very delicate because the 'irreversion' (certain *a priori*) may be difficult to observe, especially in the case of simple forms or states, the convergence between which may easily be taken for identity.

Many of the difficulties encountered in the palaeontological application of the law of irreversibility arise from a confusion between irreversibility and orthogenesis. The two ideas are patently very different. Irreversibility does not always take the form of a development in one direction (orthogenesis). Far from it. On the contrary, it admits in the history of the forms which obey it all sorts of countercurrents and circuitousness (for example, a tooth with pointed cusps may grow smaller, then become very big and take a molar form). It is from a failure to understand this pliability that some scientists have found Dollo's law[1] at fault, and others have thought it necessary to exaggerate the multiplication of genealogical lines in order to save it.

Properly understood, the law of irreversibility seems to survive all the factual objections that have so far been brought against it. It

[1] That the past is indestructible. *Tr. note.*

'succeeds' in its applications. And this success is very lucky for us: for if reversion were possible, we should find ourselves, in palaeontology, at grips with a skein of forms that we could not possibly disentangle.

L'Anthropologie, vol. XXXIII. Contribution made by Pierre Teilhard de Chardin to the meeting of the Société d'Anthropologie, of March 21, 1923.

CHAPTER IV

HOMINIZATION

INTRODUCTION TO A SCIENTIFIC STUDY OF THE PHENOMENON OF MAN

The following pages do not seek to present any philosophy directly; they set out, on the contrary, to draw their strength from the careful avoidance of all recourse to metaphysics. Their purpose is to express as objective and simple a vision as possible of humanity considered (as a whole and in its connections with the Universe) as a *phenomenon*.

What impression should we have of humanity if we were able to perceive it with the *same eyes* with which we look at the trilobites and the dinosaurs? And, inversely, how would the trilobites and the dinosaurs look to us zoologically if we could firmly place them, in our perspectives, in series with humanity? This is the question that is attempted in this study.

This question must be asked and answered. A host of scholars are occupied with human anatomy, physiology, psychology and sociology. A number of others are examining the properties or history of life and infra-human substances. Now hardly any effort has yet really been made to harmonize these two domains. Though the human and non-human are intimately linked in nature, we persistently look on them from two completely different points of view; in practice if not in theory, researchers and thinkers almost always act as if even viewed by science (although it is only concerned with appearances and antecedents) man were a certain universe, and what is not man, another. More or less alone, anatomy and morphology have tried to bring about the connection, that is to say to look boldly on man as an element in their scientific constructions. But because they have operated in a single domain, or with restricted methods, they have disparaged the value of humanity and drained the phenomenon of man of its specific properties. Usually indeed they have only obscured our vision of man's place in nature. The moment has come to resume a legitimate attempt on broader bases.

Since, as we all feel, it is wrong to preserve two different ways of seeing and valuing things, according as they fit inside or outside the zoological group in which we lie, we will try to look at man as pure natural scientists, adding nothing to him and, at the same time, taking nothing from him, but noting everything as we should in any living species discovered here or on another planet. We will then hand over the result of this 'observation' to be discussed by the professional metaphysicians.

The attempt that we suggest is not easy; if it is already difficult for the biologist and physicist to relate in their perspectives the world of beings seen 'life size' with the world of the infinitely small discovered by calculation or perceived by the miscroscope, it is a far greater labour for our minds to incorporate in a first world, seen entirely from outside (the world of minerals, plants, animals) a second world (the human world) seen almost entirely from within. Really we have to come out of our sphere and look at ourselves, at least for a moment, as if we did not know ourselves. Such a reversal, or if you prefer it, such a depersonalization is so contrary to our habits that we expect to give an idea of the action rather than perform it. Of one thing we can be sure: that we shall be rewarded for merely attempting or outlining the action, by the powerful and dramatic interest that the human commonplaces will assume, rediscovered from this point of view.

Anyone turning back to man with eyes 'dehumanized' (with the vision, for example, that comes of a long journey through the deeper zones of matter and life) will be astounded to find that humanity, so uninteresting to our bored gaze, nevertheless represents in the world of experiment: a region endowed with extraordinary properties forming a new and independent zone of the universe, and yet produced, in some way, by the maturing of the entire earth, by a process still half-conscious in which we can discover the spring and direction of the general evolution of life.

This is what we shall attempt to make at least to some extent clear.

I. THE EMPIRICAL PROPERTIES OF HUMANITY

A. *The Slight Differentiation of the Human Body*

The first characteristic of man, observed from the strictly zoological viewpoint which we have assumed, is somewhat disconcerting, and hardly seems to agree with the greatness of the perspectives we have announced. Somatically, considering the importance he has assumed in the terrestrial layer of life (or biosphere), man differs astonishingly little from the animal forms amidst which he emerged: he is very much a primate and, as such, preserves with exceptional lustre the zoological characteristics of the most ancient known mammals. Flattening of the face, increase of the cerebral part of the skull, two-footed stance coinciding with a general recasting of the body's balance but leading to no profound transformation of the bones taken singly, this is all that osteology finds to report, to distinguish man from the anthropoids. Form of limbs, number of fingers, pattern of teeth, so curiously 'primitive' that they recall an age of the world in which none of the carnivores or ungulates that today people the continents were yet alive; these are the characteristics that surprise the palaeontologist when he studies human morphology. Measured by the indices generally adopted to separate and arrange in series the other animal forms, man differs less from the apes than the bird from the reptiles, or the seal from the rest of the carnivores. He does not deserve to form zoologically more than a family or sub-order: the hominids or hominians.

This first peculiarity of man (that is to say his slight morphological differentiation, apparently disproportionate with his biological influence) is not at all a restrictive or negative characteristic, however much as it may seem so at first sight. On the contrary, *associated* with the other properties of the species, it acquires (as we shall soon see) a distinguishing and positive sense which makes it one of the most symptomatic indices of the transcendence of the phenomenon of man. We must, however, recognize that the absence of easily and absolutely distinctive features in the exterior physiognomy of our race easily inclined the classifiers to underestimate the scientific importance of our first appearance. In any case, it certainly helped to spread among natural scientists the impression that man is, for science, a composite, paradoxical being to whom one cannot safely extend the theories constructed for other animal families. Considered zoologically in his individual qualities, man is in danger of passing unperceived, and ill-recognized among the living creatures who surround him; or rather, on the contrary, he seems disconnected, sharing no common measure with them.

To grasp the greatness of the human zoological fact, we must not look superficially at its common appearances or detach it from its empirical frame, but carefully observe and consider humanity's second property, in which the astonishing originality of our animal group begins to reveal itself more distinctly, though still in the realm of tangible things: I mean man's truly unique power of extending and invading.

B *The Human Invasion*

From the simple geographical point of view, the extension of the human race is extraordinary, so extraordinary that it requires all the destructive force exercised by habit on the brightness of our impressions to prevent us from appreciating the miraculous element in the spectacle of humanity's ascent through life, the spectacle of the human tide covering the earth. Let us forget the enormous masses of living matter (microbial, planktonic or others) which form the more or less amorphous basis of the biosphere: a legitimate omission since in these lower zones, the minute size of the elements, their unorganized accumulation, their global passivity and all sorts of analogies with the lifeless circles of the world are dominant factors. Let us then confine our observations and comparisons to the upper categories of living beings, that is to say to those in which the specific form of the organism predominates over the osmotic or capillary phenomena; and the spontaneous arrangement of pairs and individuals predominates over the almost vegetable movements of floating or pullulating. Let us, moreover, make the salutary mental effort which consists in momentarily departing from our present-day earth to take a new look with the aid of geology and palaeontology at the vanished face of times gone by. Then let us return to ourselves, and we shall be almost speechless at the sight of humanity's zoological triumph.

At certain epochs, of course, we see the continents covered with different amphibians and reptiles. But these successive invasions, which rightfully rouse our admiration, are very different from the human invasion. Amphibians or reptiles, to speak of them alone, do not represent simple sheets of life. Under these somewhat factitious names, expressing a general type of life rather than a rigorously connected group, we assemble an immense variety of complex things, bringing together a very loose network of disconnected or hostile forms. Humanity, on the other hand (and here, as we said, is its prime characteristic in the eyes of natural scientists), forms a morphological whole of almost disconcerting simplicity and homogeneity. Osteologically speaking, very little distinguishes it from the other primates. Simple shades of distinction, often difficult to fix, separate, at the present day at least, the races that compose it. On the basis of this unity, composed in a manner of speaking of morphologically *almost nothing* (or rather despite this unity) men provide the zoologists with an example of a vital success beyond all comparison. If a palaeontologist from another planet were to land on our earth, presumed to be entirely fossilized, he would conclude from the simple inspection, recognition and classification of our bones, without even tracing the vestigial links and constructions with which we shall have to deal, that in the Quaternary the earth experienced a biological phenomenon of which no equivalent exists at any other zoological epoch. With prodigious rapidity (considering the very slow rhythm of general events in life) man overran the earth. Like a fire, whose very activity made him sometimes destructive, he assimilates or eliminates all life that is not of an order of size too different from his own. And if here and there other living groups appear to rival him in cosmopolitan capacities, very often he carries them with him, giving them the benefit of his strange power of dissemination and conquest. However one may view it, man is in course of transforming the rest of the animals or killing them with his shadow. Was it not Professor Osborn who lately asked with some anxiety: 'Can we save the mammals?'

Never, at any epoch, has a superior being occupied the earth as extensively as man. This is the brutal, tangible fact which should attract the attention of the greatest positivists and make them suspect a mystery. Let us continue the analysis of this fact and ask ourselves now if there is not some means of characterizing by quality (although still from a strictly experimental point of view) this sheet of humanity, so remarkable for its quantity. I think there is. Two properties absolutely new in the history of life appear with man; and one cannot ignore them scientifically without rendering the fact of his expansion inexplicable in its process and misunderstanding its ends. These are: the discovery by individuals of the artificial tool, and the realization by the collectivity of an organically linked unity. Let us study these two aspects of the phenomenon of man more closely and in turn.

c *The Tool-making Phase of Life*

Before man and outside man, the tool is not absent; far from it. But except in exceptional, almost aberrant cases, strictly limited in every instance,[1] it has the characteristic of being confused with the organism it uses. M. L. Cuénot is the first to my knowledge openly to have made this (very simple but profound) remark that all that we call zoological phyla represent only the transformation of a limb or a whole body into an instrument. The mole is a digging instrument

[1] The spider's web, for example. Recently the very curious case of certain ants has been cited, who sew leaves together, using as needles their larvae, which are endowed with the property of secreting a sort of silk.

and the horse a running instrument; the porpoise is a swimming instrument and the bird a flying instrument. In these various cases, there is an instrumental speciality by kind, by family, or by zoological order. Elsewhere, among the social insects for example, chosen individuals only are more or less totally transformed into instruments of war or reproduction. But in every case, the tool is one with the body, the living being passes into its invention.

With man everything changes. The instrument becomes external to the limb that uses it; and this entirely new method of action brings with it two consequences which entirely affect the history of life from humanity onwards: first, as is clear, a very great increase of power (in both variety and intensity), in which can be found one of the principal empirical factors in human success: secondly, and this is a more unexpected fact, a sharp fall in the apparent faculty of organisms to evolve.

This last proposition may seem a little strange. But on reflexion it will be seen that it is quite plausible, for this reason: if the somatic differentiations which preoccupy all zoologists are really bound up with the transformation of organs into instruments, man, being capable of manufacturing instruments without lending them his flesh, escapes the harsh need of transforming himself in order to act. He can therefore progress without changing his form, and vary indefinitely in his psychism without modifying his zoological type. Have we not here the partial solution of this paradox of a humanity whose 'classifying' characteristics have an insignificant value in relation to the importance of the group's role in the biosphere? Humanity seems to us much more powerful biologically than it has any right to be systematically. But we are quite mistaken in the way we extend the rules of systematics to man. To appreciate man at his true zoological value, we should not separate 'natural' from 'artificial' as absolutely as we do in our perspectives, that is to say ignore the profound connexions between the ship, the submarine, the aeroplane and the animal reconstitutions which produced the wing and the fin. By this perspective, which we will shortly resume and extend, humanity should have at least the dimensions and value of a zoological order (as befits its enormous extension); only these adaptative 'radiations' remain for humanity in some manner exteriorized. The same individual may be a mole, a bird or a fish alternately. Alone among the animals, man has the faculty of diversifying his efforts without becoming their out-and-out slave.

Thanks to its prodigious power as a tool-maker, humanity covers the continents with an almost continuous envelope of constructions; it modifies climates and the incidence of erosion; it links the seas; it distributes new substances in torrents among those in natural circulation; it alters the face of the earth to an extent which should warn us that its appearance marks the beginnings of a new phase for our planet. But this great rehandling of materials, which may rival in its geological importance the traces left on the earth's crust by the most powerful lines that have appeared within living forms, is still absolutely nothing compared with another capital fact which is revealed to us by inspection of its human layer. Humanity does not only make its instrumental domination of the earth serve to supplant all vital competition and build a world for itself; it uses it to establish a true organic unity founded in itself.

D *The Organic Unity of Humanity*

Such is, in fact, the distinctive and remarkable character of the envelope woven by humanity on the terrestrial globe that this envelope is not formed of elements coarsely juxtaposed or irregularly distributed, but tends to constitute a network informed by a common vitality.

Clearly, this conscious cohesion that we claim as peculiar to the human group does not represent a totally new phenomenon in the world. Humanity is not outside life but extends the line of life. Now just as the so-called physico-chemical matter seems incomprehensible without some deeper unity found by the corpuscular plurality in a common reality that we call sometimes ether, sometimes space-time; just as drops of water lost within the vast sheets of oceans participate in all sorts of common chemical, thermal or capillary relationships; so, at a higher degree of reality, no living mass (whether it is the whole biosphere or a fraction of it) is conceivable by science, except as permeated and animated by certain forces of solidarity which bring the particular forms into balance and control the unifying currents within the All. In the social insects especially, the collective forces acquire an extraordinary individuality and precision. Humanity, recognizably presents a unity of this type for us, when taken as a whole. Indeed it presents, as we shall repeat later on, *the same* fundamental unity. But in such unparalleled amplitude and in such detailed and increased perfection!

Humanity, one may say, is an anthill. But how can one fail to see that it differs from an anthill by two characteristics which profoundly affect its nature? First, it is universal, extending over the whole earth; and this totalitarian characteristic seems, as we shall see, to have a particular qualitative significance. Furthermore – and this is the point on which we should dwell – it is provided with special linking organs which not only assure rapid communication between the elements but little by little transform their aggregate into a sort of organism which it would be wrong to consider as simply metaphorical.

In fact, it must be repeated, our view of life is obscured and inhibited by the absolute division that we continually place between the natural and the artificial. It is, as we stated, because we have assumed in principle that the artificial has nothing natural about it (that is to say because we have not seen that artifice is *nature humanized*), that we fail to recognize vital analogies as clear as that of the bird and the aeroplane, the fish and the submarine. It is owing to this same fatal assumption that we have for years watched the astonishing system of earth, sea and air routes, postal channels, wires, cables, pulsations in the ether covering the face of the earth more closely every day without understanding. 'Merely communications for business or pleasure', they repeat, 'the setting up of useful commercial channels'. 'Not at all', we say; 'something much more profound than that: the creation of a true nervous system for humanity; the elaboration of a common consciousness, on a mass scale clearly in the psychological domain and without the suppression of individuals, for the whole of humanity. By developing roads, railways, aeroplanes, the press, the wireless, we think we are *only* amusing ourselves, or *only* developing our commerce, or *only* spreading ideas. In reality, as anyone can see who tries to put together the general design of human movements and of the movements of all physical organisms, we are quite simply continuing on a higher plane and by other means, the uninterrupted work of biological evolution.

It would be worth while to discover and define by means of a special study, the various organs, apparently artificial but really natural and profound, by which the true life of the human layer establishes itself and develops. One would then see that institutions as ordinary as our libraries, that forces as external to our bodies as education, come far closer than might be supposed to constituting a memory and heredity for humanity. Let us leave these developments aside, for it is as easy to exaggerate the analogies as it is wrong to under-estimate them and dangerous to deny them; and let us conclude our inventory of the known properties of humanity by remarking that they all emanate from two special psychic factors as observable scientifically as any other measurable energy : reflexion and (to use Edouard Le Roy's[1] expression) 'conspiration'. Reflexion, from which has arisen the discovery of the artificial instrument and, consequently, the invasion of the world by the human species: this is the faculty possessed by every human consciousness of turning in on itself in order to recognize the conditions and mechanism of its activity. 'Conspiration', from which is born the entirely new form of connection that distinguishes the human layer from all other departments of earthly life, is the aptitude of different consciousnesses, taken in a group, to unite (by language and countless other, more obscure links) so as to constitute a single All, in which, by way of reflexion, each element is conscious of its aggregation to all the rest.

Reflexion, 'conspiration': on discerning these two essentially human properties, we reach the final, but also the upper limit of what we can learn from the look that we proposed to take at man

[1] French philosopher and mathematician (1870–1954).

and life, as pure natural scientists. We have never left the ground of facts. Yet we have found the best means of sharpening our perception of all that is special and unique in the phenomenon of man. It is time therefore to start on the next phase of our inquiry. In our picture of the world, what zoological and systematic place should we give to this astounding biological production, humanity?

II. SYSTEMATIC POSITION OF HUMANITY: THE HUMAN SPHERE OR NOOSPHERE

The systematic position of man in the zoological series has appeared to us a serious problem ever since we began to measure the flagrant disproportion which exists between the slight morphological variation which led to reflected thought and the enormous impact produced by the appearance of this new faculty on the general distribution of life on earth.

We began to solve this problem when we noted that the morphological homogeneity of the human race, so remarkable when compared with the inner diversification undergone by the other animal sheets, was apparently due only to the invention of artificial tools. Humanity, as we said, like all living groups that have covered the earth at a given moment, has its inner phyla, its formal radiations or verticils: but these phyla are hidden and scattered, being represented not by lines of beings differentiated according to their specialization, but by categories of instruments which may be used successively by the same individual. When we take this into account, the human species appears a little less paradoxical. Despite its slight morphological distance from the other primates, and despite its apparent poverty in differentiated lines, it has the size, the value and the wealth not only of an 'order', but of a still vaster natural group. Zoologically, it has in itself alone, the importance not only of the carnivores or the rodents, but as much as all the mammals together. Here is the first truth that appears. But because humanity has the value of an order or even a class, does that *really* make it an order or a class? This is something quite different.

Undoubtedly this new way of understanding the position and systematic value of man would be more objective, would pay more respect to the greatness of the human fact than that of including our group, as a sub-order or family, among the apes. But, on the other hand, it would have a great drawback: it would confuse the harmony of our zoological divisions without displaying the value and specific novelty of the human species. To raise humanity to the dignity of an order or class would be to imply that it enters without change of member or form into a system of classification expressly constructed for a vital zone in which every change of activity is expressed by a change of organ. Man not only forms an exception to this law; but does so by the play of those very psychical properties which are the source of his known biological importance.

Now we have completely discovered the gravity of the problem presented to the natural sciences by the existence of man. Let it be carefully noted that when we speak of increasing the systematic value of the human group, it is not a question of tendentiously magnifying it for the purpose of some spiritual thesis. It is *simply a question of saving science*. Is it possible to safeguard at the same time both the value of the somatic characteristics adopted by systemization in order to grade beings, and the phenomenon's supreme originality (also its deep roots in the empirical world)? This is the fundamental question.

We can see only one method of escaping this difficulty; which is to state, by consideration of his unique categories, that man, connected though he is to the general development of life, represents an absolutely new phase at the termination of that development. This is to relate his appearance not only to the isolation of a class or even a predominance in the midst of life, but to something like the budding of life itself in the midst of matter. We begin to understand that the most natural division of the elements of the earth would be by zones, by circles, by *spheres*; and that among these concentric unities, organized matter itself must find its place. More clearly than the rest, the geologist Suess defined the telluric value of the mysterious living envelope which was formed at the dawn of geological time around our stellar unity. Although this view may seem at first sight both exaggerated and fantastic, what we now propose is to regard the thinking envelope of the biosphere as of the same order of zoological (or if you like telluric magnitude) as the biosphere itself. The more one considers it, the more this extreme solution seems the only honest one. Unless we give up all atempts to restore man to his place in the general history of earth as a whole without damaging him or disorganizing it, we must place him above it, without, however, uprooting him from it. And this amounts to imagining, in one way or another, above the animal biosphere a human sphere, the sphere of reflexion, of conscious invention, of the conscious unity of souls (the Noosphere, if you will) and to conceiving, at the origin of this new entity, a phenomenon of special transformation affecting pre-existent life: *hominization*. Humanity cannot be less than this without losing what constitutes its most certain physical characteristics or (what would be equally deplorable) without becoming a reality impossible to place scientifically among the other terrestrial objects. Either humanity is a fact without precedent or measure; in which case it does not fit into our natural categories, and our science is valueless. Or it represents a new turn in the mounting spiral of things; and in this case we can see no other turn to correspond with it lower down except the very first organization of matter. Nothing can be compared with the coming of reflective consciousness except the appearance of consciousness itself.

We have now reached the culminating point of our present study. Many will refuse to follow us further and declare that what we are proposing is a dream. This will only be because they will not yet have opened their eyes to the strange singularity of the human event. But let us admit that we are really speaking of a dream; it is our pleasure to pursue this dream to the end, and to see how much better the vastness and depth of the world harmonize in our dream than in the narrow reality in which our antagonists would like to confine us. To place in our scientific representation of the terrestrial world a natural division of the first order immediately below the layer of humanity is first to explain without violence the principal properties of that layer; and then to flood with the light of probability the most inward movements of biological evolution.

A. *The Birth and Structure of the Human Layer: Hominization*

Discontinuity does not mean a break. The whole perspective whose objectivity we are defending is bound up with a clear vision of this elementary truth, which is confirmed for us by countless analogies borrowed from the changes in the physical state of bodies and the development of geometrical figures.

Let us consider, for example, a cone, and in this cone let us follow the gradual diminution of its regular transverse sections in the course of a continuous movement from the base to the summit. Nothing is so different from a point as a surface. And yet, from the direction of movement chosen by us and from the properties of the cone, we discover that a given progression along the axis of the solid, having for a long time led only to a reduction in the surface areas found without modification in their nature, will at a given moment make a surface yield to a point. The cone will have produced its peak. A new order of realities is discovered and established by evolution.

Let us apply this figure to the question occupying us. What makes it difficult, we said, to understand humanity scientifically is the confusing mixture of very ancient and absolutely new characteristics that it entails. Brought up before this mixture, scholars hesitate and differ. Some, too exclusively zoological, engulf us in the lower mass of animals; they see only evolution. Others, naïvely spiritual, isolate us, making our group a sort of driftwood floating without roots on the great waters of the world; they are sensitive only to discontinuity. These are clearly two contrary exaggerations, due to an incomplete catalogue of the types of change and, consequently, of the number of zoological stages possible in the universe. In order to explain the apparent genesis of the world, they obstinately offer only two opposing terms: complete stability and continuous change. Let us decide, under pressure of the facts, to introduce into natural history the notion of single points or changes of state. We were considering a moment ago the common geometrical point formed by the slow concentration of a surface. Let us now try to look at humanity scientifically as born by an effort of total generation and, at the same time, by way of a critical point: that of the entire maturing of life, that is to say of the earth itself. Let us consequently create a new compartment in our divisions of reality, to follow that of purely animal life and yet heterogeneous to it. Let us admit, in other words, that in the structure of the terrestrial world, there are not only classes, branches, kingdoms, but that one must see in it spheres also, of which we are the last to arrive. Immediately, as can easily be seen, the human antinomy is reduced and our perspectives are no longer confused.

As we have already several times seen, if we cease to place an absolute barrier between what we call artificial and natural, the structure of the lower zoological groups appears as visibly continuing through the sheet of humanity. Not only in their forms, their gait, their individual instincts but in the collective associations and ramifications of their activities, men constitute a faunistic and zoological whole. Here is the cone and its complicated system of generating lines extending into the punctiform and indissoluble complexity of the peak. But, nevertheless, closely though the artificial can be bound to the natural, it differs from it profoundly. The artificial is the 'natural reflected', accompanied by that mysterious power of conscious cohesion between individuals which allows of their inclusion in a single layer, conscious of its connections. All the inferior manifestations of life, recognizable and unrecognizable at once, are renewed and reanimated in man. This is the unparalleled simplicity of the peak, which recasts in its rich unity the pluralism of the sheet which furls back into it.

For once geometry will have taught us a better understanding of life. Thanks to geometry we shall have put our fingers on all that is odiously absurd and fundamentally true in that phrase which drops from so many ignorant mouths and is hawked by so many pedantic textbooks: 'Man descends from the apes'. The phrase is true if one takes it to mean that, in the geological perspective, man appeared at the end of the same movement which planned and organized the lower zones of life. But it is absurd, if, as too often happens, it is taken to mean that man was born adventitiously in a narrow compartment of the biosphere and that his coming did not involve the liberation of any new terrestrial power.

Man, viewed zoologically, constitutes a new stage (perhaps a supreme stage) in the series of fundamental states through which life – and therefore terrestrial matter – is compelled to pass. As such, and despite the location of its insertion point in a determined part of the zoological tree, it represents a zone necessary for the general balance. This is the really scientific conception to which we are led by an honest inspection of all his empirical qualities. And this can, in addition, give us the best understanding of the mechanism by which life develops in general, even outside humanity also. Once the scientific reality and specific quality of the phenomenon that we have called hominization are admitted, not only does man cease to be a paradoxical excrescence in the world; but he becomes, as he normally should, the very key to our explanations of the universe. This is what now remains for us to show.

B. *Man, the Key to Evolution*

In science, even more than in philosophy, we are always inclined to look in the direction of matter, that is to say towards what is most distant in the world and strangest to our thought, to find a principle by which to understand things. This instinctive gesture, which makes us continually stretch out towards the most tangible arises from a great illusion. The simplest reflexion should convince us that in so far as the knowledge of material characteristics and the analysis of corpuscular complexities are indispensable to our inquiry into cosmic energies and the extension of our views on the structure of the universe, they can only be a slight help when our aim is to see deep into nature and the history of the universe's development.

The closer things are to us in age and nature, the more we hope to find their organization intact, and the more likely their movements are to be familiar to us, that is to say knowable. For this double reason, what we know best in the universe is life; and in life those zones that were formed last and are nearest to our zoological group. It is indisputable that, in order best to recognize the existence and procedure of an animal evolution, it is the branch of vertebrates that we must study, and on it the last bough it put forth, that of the mammals.

Why not follow this argument to the end and ask man to explain the mammals? If humanity were an absolutely heterogeneous formation, artificially stuck on to the biosphere, we could understandably treat it as an 'obscure quantity', from which we could expect no light to illuminate the rest of life. But if, as we have admitted, the human sheet, despite the profound and critical change that marks its appearance, is in fact not so divorced from the lower animal zones as not to continue their fundamental structure, then undoubtedly it is to this youngest of life's productions we must turn – the one, moreover, whose internal constitution is best known to us – in order to reconstruct the movement that gave us birth.

Let us try therefore to understand the biosphere by the Noosphere. Let us ask the nearest planes of our world and not its most distant horizons to show us the true perspective of things; and we shall be surprised to find how simple and plausible a shape the pattern of the world takes, when thus deciphered. We shall not fail to notice either how strongly, in return, this vision confirms the scientific reality of a 'hominization' of life.

On the sole condition that we regard it as organically (and not only ideally) an extension of animal life, humanity reveals the world to us in two ways: first, since it is an extremely new zoological group, almost at its point of birth, we find in it, still in process of formation (and therefore we cannot deny their evolutionary nature) the principal characteristics that mark the oldest and most fixed zoological unities; and secondly, since it is *our own* group, we are able to discover (in the very movement that pulls and diversifies the human species) the hidden springs (lying in our own deep consciousness) of that evolution which we have accepted as true in the world outside us.

1. *Biological evolution traced in the present-day course of Humanity.* When, after an inquiry laboriously pursued through the maze of living and vanished animal forms, we decide to bring our gaze back to human history, we have to admit that our eyes would not have had to wander so far in search of the fact and fundamental laws of evolution if they had been better accustomed at the beginning to perceive the outlines and connections of living beings. The observation of zoological types gathered from the four quarters of space and time has shown us many things about the law of distribution by which organisms were scattered over the surface of the earth and through the geological beds. But we can see all the harmonies it has shown us, all the paradoxes it has forced us to admit, reproduced in different colours but in the same details in us and around us. We have no need to look outside Humanity.

Transformism, as an empirical construction, inclines us to think that living groups appear, succeed and interrupt one another, rather like waves. Each group, it seems, is born in a restricted zoological and geographical domain, beginning with a small number of individuals that have reached the same organic stage and similarly conditioned surroundings; and from here it spreads with more or less success over the surface of the earth. Indiscernible at first, because so small, it gradually assumes an importance which allows it to leave in the form of fossils, indelible traces of its passage; it grows, but at the same time it disintegrates and hardens. Broken up by the extension of its sheet, which must differentiate in order to conform to the necessities of its internal equilibrium, it sends out verticils of forms adapted to special conditions of activity or habitat; and each of these forms, like a shoot that has lignified or an over dentated leaf, soon shows itself unfit, from lack of suppleness or excessive complication, for any new morphological attainment. Thus dissociated or immobilized, the class, order, kind or species cease to expand; they first fragmentate and finally disappear among younger and more vigorous living sheets, where their isolated remains may trail on almost indefinitely as wreckage.

Here, briefly sketched, is the picture of the developments of Life that zoologists have succeeded in reconstructing. Did they really discover it outside themselves? Or quite simply, and unconsciously, have they recognized and expressed themselves in it? One thing is certain: in making this design they have reproduced the portrait of humanity feature by feature.

Man, in so far as we can understand him scientifically, appeared very humbly, in a narrowly limited region of life and earth. Deeply rooted among the primates, probably born in a very small space of the Ancient World, he succeeded, almost without notable morphological changes, in invading and dominating the entire earth. We sometimes wonder uneasily how species and kinds can really be formed. Why not learn the lesson from an example that is close to us? Did not man, who is not divided from other animals by much more than the interval of a mutation, become more powerful and (to a seeing eye) more differentiated than an order or even a class? To guide or confirm our imagination, baffled by the envisaged consequences of transformism, and powerless to face all these 'beginnings', let us take a look at humanity. Many people will not know how or will not wish to take this look. Close though it is to us, compared with other origins, the birth of humanity is still a distant and bitterly controversial fact. Let us leave it therefore; and for something certain and indisputable, let us look still nearer ourselves. The general movement has its replicas. Right in the midst of the human sheet, the zoological waves continue endlessly and in more and more elementary groups, to be born and to meet. By countless reductions of the fundamental evolution of the species, races and civilizations succeed one another within humanity. They arise, spread, cross in different directions, and die; and like the beach after a series of ebb tides, each continent is fringed with the foam and debris successively left behind by their waves. No one will attempt to deny that these reduced harmonics of the great human oscillation are of an evolutionary nature.

What do they show us but the repetition, and therefore the confirmation or explanation, of what we can learn by observing the non-human layers of life?

In the history of the peoples who grow or supplant one another, we sometimes manage to distinguish the tribe or population whose success has given birth to a great civilization. But more often we come against the implacable law which, preventing our vision of beginnings (too humble to be perceptible), allows us to see the movement of the past only in the form of a series of fixed elements with sizeable maxima and established successes. And here, exactly reproduced, is the continuous distribution of beings so familiar to palaeontology. Let us now take a detailed look at the swarm of human branches; and we shall be able to collect at will the different kinds of history by which the complexities and difficulties of the zoological lines arise. First of all, there is the impoverished, stagnant race, that has not changed since prehistoric times and seems likely to perish rather than change; and here, beside it, the vigorous, conquering people which grows continuously, draws all the sap to itself and seems to represent not only the active extremity of a secondary branch, but the very leading shoot of humanity. Here now are the simple groups, in which everyone is doing the same thing, and here are the complicated, inventive nations in which the individuals divide into all sorts of specialized categories. Here too are the long periods of immobility, the winter of the peoples during which nothing stirs, and here are the phases of blossoming, in the course of which, mysteriously and at a thousand different points of the human layer, suddenly the same ideas, the same aspirations, the same inventions germinate. Here, in its turn, is the long series of vital declines: the exhaustion and ageing of the races, their collapse into lassitude, their encrustation beneath social envelopes which have become gilded and sterile castes, their stiffening under collective and individual routine; and here, finally, above this neo-matter in constant process of forming and rejecting, vast and ancient matter reappears. As imponderable in appearance as the inorganic world beneath the impassive mask of statistical laws, the determinism of great numbers and the painful friction of unorganized masses cover and level the quivering inner sheet of the Noosphere.

We always persuade ourselves that these analogies are literary comparisons. Why do we not see *that they are the actual reality*? If we want to understand life scientifically, we must consequently not hesitate to ask questions of ourselves?

2. *The psychic Essence of Evolution*. When, at the beginning of these pages we pointed out the natural quality beneath the human artifice, we hinted at the explanation of life to which the views here developed on hominization will lead. The tool, as we have repeatedly said, is the equivalent in the human series of the differentiated organ in the animal series; the equivalent, that is to say the true homologue and not the superficial imitation born of a commonplace convergence. But once this equivalence between the results of an operation that we call industrial in man and organic in the animal is admitted, we are led to suppose some equivalence and relationship in the operation itself; for *the power of invention corresponds to the thing invented*. And we see immediately, as through an open breach, psychic energies invading the domain of transformism from within.

It is certainly not a question of anthropomorphically transporting the methods and reflexion characteristic of the Noosphere into the lower spheres of life. It is not a question either of lazily reverting to a consideration of the vital forces which would excuse us from an analytical search for the elementary energies unconsciously woven by life as a cover for its need to perceive and act. Our meaning is that in noting the connections between man's activity with his tools and the natural activities of life, we are led to conclude that this use of tools is only a transformed extension, a superior aspect of these natural activities. Our aspirations and powers of invention reveal themselves as this same organogenic power of life 'hominized'. And, reciprocally, the whole evolutionary process of the organic world becomes comprehensible when placed in analogy with the developments of our human world.

We are far from suggesting that this is a new perspective, and claim for it only an empirical value. It has, however, patently the prime advantage of harmonizing with what we see outside us in the birth, development and death of zoological lines; phenomena, as we have said, which all so curiously remind us of what is going on around us in the domain of ideas, languages, physical discoveries, and social institutions. But it has a more considerable advantage still: it tells us what constitutes the hidden motor or movement of life. Let us admit (as we do) that organic life under cover of the determinisms analysed by biological science is, like our conscious life, an infinite fumbling and perpetual discovery. But we must take one further step. Why do we ourselves seek and why do we invent? In order to *be better*; and, above all, in order to *be more*, stronger and more conscious. Why, therefore, does all the rest of life stir and strive? In order – there can be no doubt – to be more, to understand better. It must be so, for life invents! And here is the lightning-flash that illuminates the biosphere to its depths from the moment when natural contact is re-established between its lowest layers and its human envelope. By a method that scarcely rises above that of simple observation we are able to make contact with the intuitions to which metaphysics is becoming increasingly wedded. *Nothing really exists in the Universe except myriads of more or less obscure spontaneities, the compressed swarm of which gradually forces the barrier separating it from liberty.* From top to bottom of the series of beings, everything is in motion, everything is raising itself, organizing itself in a single direction, which is that of the greatest consciousness. This is why since the origins of life nervous systems in every branch of animals have always been increasing and perfecting themselves to the point that never since the dawn of geological time has the mass of cerebralized matter been larger.

It must be maintained that scholars are abundantly right in setting a high value on the marks life makes on living flesh, or leaves on fossilized remains. But let them beware, in the course of their work, not to lose or even to reverse the sense of the values they are considering. It is not the tissues and bones that have made living creatures. Bones and tissues are only the shells in which psychic tendencies have successively clothed themselves; and these tendencies were the product always of the same fundamental aspiration to know and act.

And so we are brought to a better understanding of this single critical point encountered by life on earth on the appearance of humanity. On account of a property, difficult for our reason to understand, but the reality of which is vouched for by the facts, we observe that animal psychism[1] could not continue indefinitely to unify without finding itself as if compelled to a change of nature. In the act of diminution, the sections of the cone must be succeeded by its pointed tip. Similarly, by virtue of the organic laws of the movement animating it, terrestrial consciousness has attained a new stage. By coming closer together, its generating lines, hitherto unarranged, have united in a definite centre; and all at the same time, it has acquired the three fundamental properties that characterize the elements of the Noosphere; it has seen itself by reflexion; it has found itself capable of collaborating in its own further progress *by invention*; and finally it has become fit to conquer, by spiritual relationship and sympathy, the dissolvent effect that accompanies all individualization. It has appeared as a possible element in a sort of higher organism which might form itself, one from all, *by conspiration*. Now we see a little better why man is distinguished at once so much and so little from the great mass of other animals. Specialized at the very axis of life, he has had no need (and it would have been an irremediable weakness for him) to assume any of the particular forms which zoologists see as the distinguishing marks and advantages of other animal groups. In him, progress is made not by acquisition of particular organs, but by development of the very sources of action. In this way he has kept his liberty of movement at the maximum. In the incredibly varied jungle of animal forms, he has remained (even judged from the simple, zoological point of view) the vertebrate, the mammal, the living being, *par excellence*.

[1] Sustained, of course, by some deep creative force. If we do not speak more explicitly of this force, it is, we repeat, because our purpose is to follow the shape of the apparent curve of phenomena without examining the metaphysical conditions of its existence.

Most probably, the external human type will not change again. Life on earth, the purest sap of which has passed to humanity, does not seem to have in reserve any form that can ever relay our race in its climb towards the highest consciousness.

Hominization has unleashed an immense force on the world: this is the material fact that we have studied so far. But at the same time it has introduced, correlatively, into the conduct of life formidable risks, in which human knowledge discovers the problem of evil at its origins. We will conclude our sketch of the grandeurs and novelty of the phenomenon of man with a brief examination of this fact.

Till man's appearance, beings, ignorant of their strength and future, worked unconsciously (and in consequence faithfully) for the general progress of life. Attracted by immediate needs or urged by an obscure instinct, they unconsciously went straight ahead. Physical evil spurred them on, for there exists an initial disunity deeply rooted in matter, which is the source of pain and death. But the infinite fumblings of life worked patiently to reduce these disorders. And though tendencies to inertia and indiscipline (precursory signs of the times to come) already manifested themselves in individuals, the enormous bulk of living beings, polarized as a whole towards more or better being, raised itself unhesitatingly as a mass towards the higher regions of being. At that time life, poorly armed against outside enemies, had nothing to fear from itself. Its great danger and at the same time its great strength, revealed themselves on the day when, in giving birth to humanity, it became conscious of itself. Man with his freedom to lend or refuse himself to the battle represents the fearful faculty of scanning and criticizing life. When man opens his eyes on the world, he perceives and compares its pains and advantages. He distinguishes the two iron laws to which the animals bowed incomprehendingly (and hence without suffering) the necessity of denying themselves in order to grow and the necessity of death, and feels (the more deeply the more truly he is man) their burden and horror. Then, turning by reflection towards the universal reality which gave him birth, he finds himself obliged since he thinks to judge his own mother. Inevitably, by virtue of the uncontrollable forces presiding over the conscious burgeoning of the world, the temptation to revolt and the dangers that it brings for the future of existence, appear at a given moment in the universe. Before the painful effort to continue, before the trial of death which must be met, courage or faith may fail us. In the depths of our prison we may recoil in savage isolation; or by a vain effort to break our chains, we may dissipate ourselves in desperate activities; or to still our anguish we may drown ourselves in pleasure. And immediately the impulse of life becomes slow, wavers and declines.

This crisis of human activity is, by its nature, as old as man. It is abundantly clear that we must not confine it to a few brief instants or only to the origins of our race. Born with the intellect, the temptation to revolt must constantly change and *grow* with it. And this is why it has never appeared more acute and more universal than today.

The present zoological era, as we were saying a moment ago, is full of extraordinary novelty. It is positively renewing the face of the earth. If we rightly understand at its just value the moral battle being fought before our eyes, we must go even further and declare that within this human era *we are actually passing through a singular critical epoch*. At each epoch in history, the last men to arrive have always found themselves in possession of an accumulated heritage of knowledge and science, that is to say faced with a more conscious choice between fidelity and infidelity to life, between Good and Evil. But just as in the life of individuals there are certain hours of awakening from which, by a sudden transformation, we emerge as adults, so in the general development of human consciousness, there come centuries during which the drama of initiation into the world, and consequently the inner struggle, suddenly occur. We are living at such a moment.

The prehistorians have observed it for a long time. If we try to fit our contemporary history into the general pattern of the human past (by applying the same method that has served us for fitting the human past into the general evolution of the earth) we must conclude that we are standing, at the present moment, not only at a change of century and civilization, but at a *change of epoch*. Up to recent times nothing had essentially modified the conditions established in the prehistoric human layer by the coming of the agricultural peoples. No new source of energy had been discovered; man continued to use the same fire that his palaeolithic fathers had lit; and he remained in fact limited in his views of the universe, weak in the midst of natural energies, dispersed in his efforts to achieve union. And then suddenly, prepared by the introduction of scientific and experimental methods, a great change begins. Man discovers the laws of chemical energy, he conquers the powers of the ether, he investigates the atomic and stellar abysses; he discovers endless extensions of his history into the past, infinite increases in his power of acting on matter. Infinite hopes open up for his spiritual achievement. Here, properly speaking, is the beginning of a new cycle. The Neolithic age, which is hardly over, is succeeded all around us, at this moment, by the age of industry, the age of Internationals, and at the same time, to a marked degree, the age of strikes and revolutions. Not only because of humanity's place in life, but because of our century's place in human history we now stand at a prodigiously interesting epoch in the earth's story. Never so conscious of their individual and collective force, but never so pervaded either by dislike of the forces of injustice and horror of irremediable death, men have once more to choose before engaging in the service of evolution. 'Does life which has made us what we are deserve that we should extend it further?' At this present hour the great effort of hominization arouses this acute moral question in the heart of us all.

In this deep and universal confusion, where shall we find the light by which to see and the strength to follow the light? Only by means of a clearer and more realistic view of the great cause from which we might be tempted to declare our independence. A crisis of cosmic nature and magnitude, the social ferment which is today pervading human populations can only be dominated and guided by a clearer and more conscious faith in the supreme value of evolution.

It is continually repeated that evolution is a wicked doctrine, a fit vehicle for materialism and ideas of universal struggle. To comfort the world and teach it morality, our opponents seek to reduce and discredit this theory. A fatal tactic, we would cry, and designed only to accelerate the crisis that we are anxious to overcome. You are afraid of the desire for independence and pleasure which is spreading like wildfire through the world. You are seeking a means of disciplining individualism and abolishing cowardice. You will find no alternative but to exalt in men's eyes the greatness of the whole which they fail to recognize, and whose success might be impaired by their egoism. So long as only their individual advantage seems to them at stake in earth's adventure, and so long as they only feel compelled to work because of external commands, the men of our time will never submit their mind and will to anything greater than themselves. Explain to them, on the contrary, unhesitatingly the greatness of the current of which they are part. Make them feel the immense weight of committed efforts for which they are responsible. Compel them to see themselves as conscious elements in the complete mass of beings, inheritors of a labour as old as the world, and charged with transmitting the accumulated capital to all those who are to come. Then, at the same time, you will have overcome their tendency to inertia and disorder, and shown them what they perhaps worshipped without giving it a name.

For this is the supreme purpose of the present human phase of terrestrial history; that the normal crisis which has struck us shall be compensated by the renewal and growth of our beings, in the double form of a necessity and an attraction, of a divine pressure emanating from the Absolute.

There is, as we have said, only one method to keep the indisciplined crowd of human monads bound to the task of life: to make the passion for the whole prevail in them over elementary egoism, that is to say practically to increase their consciousness of the general evolution of which they are a part. But why should they submit themselves to this evolution if they are not travelling towards something that is *for ever*? More and more distinctly the dilemma in which human activity stands is revealed to the least of workers on earth.

Either life is moving to no accumulation and consummation of its work: and then the world is absurd, self-destroying, condemned by the first reflective glance which it has attained at the cost of immense efforts; and then revolt is with us again, no longer as a temptation but *as a duty*.

Or else something (someone) exists, in which each element gradually finds, by reunion with the whole, the completion of all the saveable elements that have been formed in its individuality; and then it is worth while bending and even devoting oneself to labour; but with an effort that takes the form of adoration.

Thus the interior equilibrium of what we have called the Noosphere requires the presence *perceived by individuals* of a higher pole or centre that directs, sustains and assembles the whole sheaf of our efforts. Would it be going too far and leaving the empirical realm to introduce at this point a new observation? Is not this divine centre, required by the nature of things to justify our activity, precisely He whose influence makes itself positively felt in us by the tendency to greater cohesion, justice and brotherhood which has been for the last century the most comforting symptom to be seen around us in the inner development of humanity?

A wind of revolt is passing through our minds, it is true. But, born of the same growths of conscience, another breeze is blowing through the human masses; one that draws us all by a sort of living affinity towards the splendid realization of some foreseen unity. Disputed, suspect and often scorned, unitary aspirations in politics, in thought, in mysticism, arise everywhere around us; and because their subject is not what is material and plural but what is spiritual and common to all in each one of us, no force of routine or egoism seems capable of arresting them; irresistibly they infiltrate and gradually dissolve old forms and false barriers.

It is our wish to seek in that supreme manifestation of biological forces surrounding us, a final and direct reason for admitting the distinct existence and believing in the certain future of a Noosphere. The infallible pull which, overcoming from the beginning the whims of chance, the disorder of matter, the sloth of the flesh and the pride of the spirit, has created man and continues to construct almost perceptibly, out of our souls a higher reality – this pull – I would say – gathers and consecrates (in fact and in faith) all that the analysis of the phenomenon of man has revealed to us in the course of this study. By its continuity it demonstrates the coherence of the deep movement which, starting from matter, culminates in spirit. By the higher form it assumes in our faculties for reflection and love, it marks the type of consummation represented in terrestrial life by the awakening of human thought. Finally, by its very appearance and perpetual rebirth, it provides evidence that a vital link has once and for all been established between our efforts, which hasten, and the upper goal, which directs the progress of hominization.

Unpublished, Paris, May 6, 1923.

CHAPTER V

THE TRANSFORMIST PARADOX

ON THE LATEST CRITICISM OF TRANSFORMISM BY M. VIALLETON

In the course of the last thirty years, palaeontological discoveries have been multiplying beyond all expectation. Extensive excavations undertaken in America, Asia, Africa have extended our knowledge of past life beyond all expectations. Primary reptiles of the Karoo, dinosaurs of the Rocky Mountains and the Gobi, proboscidians of the Fayum, large simians of the Siwaliks, numberless and so far unnamed ungulates in the far west of China or America, form so many new groups, scarcely investigated, in which we see with astonishment the immensity and fecundity of living nature.

Through this enormous proliferation of terrestrial life, palaeontology continues to find its way without difficulty. However vast and complicated the biosphere may appear, the great currents that swept it long ago, leaving almost no trace, and those that still make themselves felt, in their death or birth, around us, become more and more recognizable. Not only the general succession of the great animal groups, but the development of particular zoological families outline themselves with growing distinctness. Not so long ago, the only great phyletic series that transformism could present was that (somewhat painfully assembled) of horses. Now we know in its broad outlines (to confine ourselves to the mammals) the history of the camelids, the primates, the proboscidians, the rhinoceroses, the titanotheres and numerous carnivores. We may say that in the group of higher animals, there does not exist today a single absolutely isolated form. Today, more than ever, the dominant impression made by the spectacle of life remains, whatever we may say, one of a single development beneath an extraordinary variety of forms.

It would seem under these conditions that on a definitely known and cleared terrain, the science of vanished living forms had only to glide forward by the effortless application of fixed laws of classification and filiation to new fossils as they appeared.

This reliance on attained truth, even if desirable, would not be human. No more in biology than in physics does reality permit us to say that it is ever exhausted. At the precise moment when we think we have reached the bottom, it suddenly extends, facing us with a new realm to explore.

Once upon a time natural historians had no eyes except for those natural links and sequences which, first perceived by Lamarck and Darwin, freed their science from the cold, abstract Linnean categories. If they could return today to our museums in London, New York or Paris, the first transformists would no doubt believe in the pure and simple triumph of their theories. And yet if they were to question us, who are performing the resurrections that fulfil their wishes, they would find that our minds remain unsatisfied because, beyond what might seem to them as full light, we see new shadows extending. Observed from afar and as a whole, as we were saying a moment ago, life is still one, and its phyla give still greater evidence of continuity than formerly. But we have thought fit to examine it more closely. And now, under our minute inspection, the boasted unity and continuity of living forms appears to become disjointed. Just as when the physicists attacked decimals, they found divergences between their measurements and the finest mathematical laws of the universe, so naturalists, on more closely examining the morphology of living and vanished creatures, have perceived disturbing anomalies.

To begin with the phyla, none of the forms that we place in series in each phylum really stands end to end with the one that follows it. It always presents some 'inadaptive' characteristic, some particular specialization, which takes it out of the line, and makes it diverge a little. The classical history of the *Hipparion*, once placed among the ancestors of the horse because of its lateral toes, but much more complicated than the horse in the form of its teeth, appears to be repeated in a less accentuated form in the majority of our genealogical constructions. The more completely we know the fossils we are cataloguing, the more difficulty we have in maintaining the fine regularity of their distribution. Seen under a magnifying glass, our purest phylogenic lines show themselves to be formed of little overlapping segments which envelop and relay but do not exactly prolong one another.

If now, instead of neighbouring forms placed on the same phylum (that of the equids for example) we compare two forms, one belonging to a principal branch, the other to a derived one, not only is there the divergence foreseen by the transformist theory, but this divergence is such that we cannot see how, mechanically, the transition could have taken place from one to the other. In an important book, recently examined here by M. Manquat,[1] that eminent anatomist M. Vialleton pitilessly analysed the impossibilities facing a close morphology should it attempt to derive a bird by stages from a reptile, a bat from a climbing insectivore, a seal from a walking carnivore.

In conclusion, and this is what we shall call the 'transformist paradox'. the latest achievements of palaeontology have led us to discover rigidity and fixedness beneath the supple and mobile. Life perceived by the first advances of science as a fluid continuity, resolves itself, as our researches progress further, into independent and discontinuous terms.

Disturbing though this paradox may be, its discovery should not have made the natural scientists doubt the soundness of their first discovery. Is it not the essence of all real movement (spatial, chemical, biological) that it can be broken up under analysis into motionless elements?

[1] *Membres et ceintures de Vertébrés tétrapodes. Critique morphologique du Transformisme* (Limbs and girdles of the tetrapod vertebrates. A morphological criticism of transformism). See *La Revue des Questions Scientifiques,* April 1924, p. 370.

In fact, surprised though M. Depéret and Mr. Osborn, for example, may be at seeing the phylum of the proboscidians – apparently so well established – dissolve under their learned hands into countless separate genealogical series, neither of them is at all doubtful of the firm evidence for a certain transformism. The great majority of natural scientists agree with them. Intrigued by life's curious aptitude for betraying no movement if one tries to catch its mobility in a restricted sphere, they do not consider themselves bound on that account to renounce their fertile and irreplaceable theories of biological evolution.

Certain people, however (and they, I observe, are not palaeontologists) prove disconcerted when they discover Zeno on their territory. M. Vialleton, in the book alluded to, is particularly pessimistic: according to him, we know nothing more about life since the work of the transformist school than we did before. Emanating from such an authority, this confession of discouragement has, of course, been loudly quoted in circles quite foreign to the natural sciences. Some have even gone so far as to proclaim 'the collapse of transformism'!

In order to temper these excesses, and explain and justify the faith in evolution which remains, so far as I know, the best guide and the strongest support of all present-day palaeontologists, I propose in the following pages:

(1) To show that the transformist paradox, if proved, leaves the fundamental views and prerequisites of transformism entirely untouched.

(2) To diminish the force of this paradox by showing that if, on the one hand, it may possibly be due to a simple effect of perspective, it may also, on the other, cause us to make very profitable progress in the ideas we form about the history of living beings.

I will conclude by recalling, once more, the nature of the essential postulate which underlies the theory of transformism, and gradually detaches itself from it; which is one that no modern scientist could possibly renounce without contradicting his own researches.

A. *What is not Threatened by the Transformist Paradox.*
   The 'Natural Place' of Beings

Let us admit, for a start, that the contradictory appearances of supple movement and fixed rigidity, presented alternately by life according as one looks at it from far or near, as a whole or in detail, is not a simple play of light. Let us admit further that, in this contradiction between our experiences, reality is entirely on the side of the fixed and rigid, so that the sequence of living species, as we know them better, must always and increasingly reveal itself to us as a series of compartments, arranged according to a pattern of movement, but each motionless and each walled off from the other.

In this hypothesis, the most unfavourable possible to transformism, what would happen to the work of the evolutionary natural scientists? What would remain of the brilliant, but transitory transformist period?

There would remain at least one huge capital fact, of which the opposition strangely fails to feel the force or measure the consequences: the fact of the *natural distribution of living forms*.

However preponderant the proportion of statics reintroduced at a certain time by naturalists into their patterns of animal and vegetable life, thanks to the gatherers and reconstructors of fossils one definite acquisition will remain, that in no case has a perissodactyl or artiodactyl limb existed that has not been preceded by polydactyl feet – a cutting carnassial (like that of the weasels, hyenas or cats) that has not been prepared for by carnassials with three-pointed cusps (like that of the genets or dogs), a tusk (whether of the narwhal, the walrus or the elephant) the sketch of which is not to be found in an abnormally developed canine or incisor – a nasal or frontal horn that has not grown on a skull at first undefended, etc. etc. Whatever may be the reason for this condition its existence is absolutely beyond doubt. Nothing is constructed in living organisms except on the basis of a sketch. Never do really viable and stable morphological characteristics appear by chance; all take their place in a rigorously determined order.

84

Here it is of small importance, I repeat, whether the animal species in whom the characteristics in question evolve continue one another by a bond of generation, or each forms a sort of morphological dead end, from which no individual escapes. The interesting thing to observe at this moment is that the zoological species, even if they form, as is said, isolated scales, in every case cover and overlap one another like the leaves of conifers, in such a way as to construct (or at least to simulate) a stem, a tree, a bush, if you wish; in every case a regular and coherent whole. In a recent study,[1] we have tried to fix, independent of any transformist hypothesis, that scaly structure of phyla in the case of the primates. What we have tried to do for the simians could just as well be done for any other living group. In fact it is extraordinary to see how easily, throughout the whole zoological realm, the overlapping or feathered structure of living beings continues from the smallest to the largest zoological group. Closest together in the groups nearest to us (mammals among the vertebrates, man among the mammals) the scales or branches rapidly space out as we go deeper into the abysses of the past. But the general symmetry does not cease to be visible. Even when entirely cut off, to our eyes, from the principal trunk, the various branches preserve in their shape, an appearance of relationship which makes them as infallibly recognizable as the elements of a single building as are two boughs torn from the same tree. It is certainly not by chance that mammals isolated in Patagonia produced their solipeds during the Tertiary, or that the didelphids, cut off in Australia since the Secondary, produced their mole, their hedgehog, their rodents and their carnivores – or, more generally, that each zoological stem, left to itself, spreads in a verticil of forms, some adapted for running, others for flight or dwelling in trees, or living underground or swimming. On seeing this capacity for regular proliferation, how can we not be sure, despite all secondary difficulties, that the zoological groups form an organic part of a single natural entity?

This single observation should be enough to limit for ever the

[1] *Palaeontology and the Appearance of Man* (Revue de Philosophie, March–April 1923) Teilhard de Chardin, *The Appearance of Man*, p. 33.

field of transformist polemics: in whatever aspect one observes the assembly of animal forms, one immediately sees, in both mass and detail, an organized harmony either immediately evident or increasingly pursued. Before all hypotheses, from a simple inspection of the geometrical distribition of living beings on the earth, one is forced to admit that no zoological species could have made its physical appearance at any other time or place than it did. In other words, by virtue of the total play of the astronomical, geological and biological factors of our world, each living form occupies an exact position; it has a *natural place*, from which it could not be uprooted without destroying the whole balance of the universe.

In view of this, I ask if it is legitimate seriously to state that we have learnt nothing new about life by virtue of systematic classification. Is it really nothing to know that the bat (however complete the morphological mould from which it seems to have come) appeared beside the climbing insectivores, or the seal among the terrestrial carnivores, or birds in the immediate neighbourhood of reptiles? Admittedly we have not yet formed a distinct idea of the phases of any of their metamorphoses. But two principal points have nevertheless been gained, *which were unsuspected in the time of Linnaeus*. Today we are sure that there is a biological solution to the problem of the genesis of the *Chiroptera*, the pinnipeds and the birds; and we are sure also that this solution is contained in a known field.

Certainly a scientific explanation exists for the origin of species, for neither the bat, the seal, nor the birds would have a natural place in the universe if they did not appear there by virtue of a collection of analysable and experimental factors. And the field in which to search for this explanation is already found: it lies between two geological epochs, and within perfectly determined zoological groups.

In view of this, when I hear unbridled talk about the great transformist illusion, I declare that I fail to understand what the criticism means. An illusion, the flowing of one zoological species into another? I grant it. We have already discussed this hypothesis. An illusion, the general ascent of forms towards increasing consciousness and spontaneity? I grant this too. This view is too deeply steeped in

86

philosophy, in a type of mysticism even, to persuade any pure scientist that the modifications of life are not just a simple labour of diversification. But an illusion, the ordered, organized, ineluctable distribution of living beings through time and space? I deny this with all the strength of my palaeontological experience.

One moment, you may say. Here you are fighting an imaginary opponent. No one dreams of contesting the geometrical distribution of which you speak. It is too evident for any natural scientist not to see it. Is that so? Then how is it you do not see that by this one concession you are rescuing the thing you set out to destroy? We have just said: a *natural* grouping of animals in time and space is an assurance that living beings have come into the universe through a *natural* door; and a *natural* origin for livings beings is the guarantee that there is a *natural* reason, (that is to say, a scientific one) for the phenomenon of their appearance in succession.[1] But is transformism fundamentally anything but the belief in a *natural* link between animal species? By the sole fact that you admit such a link in living nature you readmit the whole evolutionary point of view into your perspectives. And I recognize that you could not do otherwise. Broadly understood, as it should be, transformism is now a hypothesis no longer. It has become the form of thought without which no scientific explanation is possible. That is why, even in an absolutely unexpected form, it will inevitably continue to direct and animate the morphology of the future.[2]

What we have just said should already be enough to explain why palaeontologists are right, despite the enigmatic behaviour of life, in remaining faithful to evolutionary views. Even in a universe in which the animal species succeed one another by leaps, without any direct filiation, it would still be necessary to find a scientific explanation for

[1] It will be understood, I think, that throughout this sentence, the term 'natural' (used as the opposite of 'artificial') does not apply any species of limitation on the influence of the Primal Cause. See further, the note on p. 102.

[2] In face of transformism, as just defined, the expectant or agnostic attitude is not even permissible. The problem argued among scientists is no longer that of discovering *if* species appear as the outcome of another, but *how* they do so.

the order followed by these discontinuities; that is to say, to find a law of evolution. But before renouncing the old and simple idea of phyla in which the successive stages introduce one another by generation in the ordinary sense, we must still consider more closely whether the transformist paradox should really, as we have hitherto conceded, be solved in favour of the stability and independence of the elements whose series forms the vital movement, or whether it is not this stability and independence that are illusory.

Before any analysis of detail, this second position is by far the more attractive. No one, I think, who has had actually to concern himself with systematic classification will contradict me on this point: the first, instinctive impression made by the prolonged observation of living organisms is, incontrovertibly, that there is an organic bridge from one species to another. How can we allow, for example, that the humerus and astragalus of the mammals have been several times independently invented by nature?[1] From the positions occupied, now and in the past, by living beings on earth, there follows almost necessarily the existence of a passage between them. '*Ex situ, transitus.*' Of course, on reading M. Vialleton, I am impressed by the mechanical difficulties in the way of an evolutionary passage from an ordinary insectivore to a bat or a mole, from an ungulate to a manatee. But when I see '*in natura rerum*' some of the changes declared impossible taking place periodically with variable intensity in very different phyla (for this is the case in all 'adaptive' radiations); when I find for example, tunnelling the steppes of Mongolia, an authentic rodent, the *Myospalax*, whose burrowing limbs are exactly half-way between those of a rat and a mole, I ask myself with some relief if the mechanical impossibilities attributed to classical transformism are calculated in the same manner as those which might be advanced to prove that a locomotive cannot run on rails. Life is

---

[1] Despite his deliberate agnosticism on the subject of evolution, M. Vialleton, speaking of the origin of the *Chiroptera*, cannot avoid saying that, in order to form them, nature 'probably began with ordinary mammalian prototypes' (p. 421), a current proof, be it said in passing, of the impossibility encountered by any true natural scientist of 'exorcising' the transformist forms of thought.

certainly much more supple and fertile in inventions than we suppose. Would it not be puerile to deny metamorphoses the evidence for which imposes itself on us almost ineluctably, under the pretext that we have not yet succeeded in analysing them?

Let us try, therefore, by preserving the old hypothesis of transformism through descent, to explain how it can happen that the movement which theoretically guides living beings in their successive evolutions is so vast or so intermittent that we can never in fact capture anything but immobile and rigid fragments in our laboratories.

B. *Attempt at an Interpretation of the Transformist Paradox*

A first means of explaining the bizarre mixture of continuity and discontinuity presented by life under scientific analysis may be sought in the indubitable fact that the number of zoological species whose stages can be plotted in series in the history of animal development is incomparably larger than we imagine. What we call a line, that of the horses or elephants for instance, has not been just a simple living fibre, nor even a well-defined bundle of easily distinguishable forms. Actually, a phylum is composed of an immense quantity of morphological units, connected at random by all the freaks of geographical migration and fossilization. If we could manage to isolate a thread of that skein and follow it for a long way through the geological epochs, we should note the existence of a true morphological continuity between the elements. But in fact this favourable chance has never occurred. In the successive sections (scattered and with great lacunae) that we are able to make at different levels on a single zoological branch, we find sometimes one fibre, sometimes another, probably never the same one on two occasions. Our general series therefore are each no more than an ideal axis, zigzagging roughly within the real bundle of zoological species. Our phyla are approximate constructions, composite and manufactured from elements borrowed from different organic units.

At a first approximation, this method of procedure has no

defects since the representation it gives us of the evolution of living forms is, by and large, similar to the curve actually followed by nature. But if we set out to make a detailed criticism of our construction, we are bound to notice that its elements do not exactly correspond, that there is some deviation between them. Clearly this should not astonish us; the movement of life is very real; but our method of work is still too clumsy for us to be able to uncover it exactly.

There seems no doubt that this first resolution of the transformist paradox is valid in a great number of cases. Quite simply, the same thing has happened to the zoologists as happened to the physicists and astronomers: an increase in precision makes them temporarily doubt the fine and simple truth arrived at on the evidence of a more naïve observation of facts. We cannot see the wood for the trees. However, even after these explanations, the principal difficulties encountered by transformism today in the application of its theories still remain. We are beginning to understand the dislocations that our best genealogical series undergo under sufficient magnification. We do not yet see why these series appear before us as entities almost entirely formed, and sometimes extend indefinitely without a sensible modification of their characteristics.

The key to this double mystery is probably to be sought in a very generalized theory of 'mutations', supplemented by some very simple considerations of the alterations imposed on our perspectives of the past by the mechanism of fossilization, and supported (whatever may be said) by a psychic interpretation of evolution.

1. We often speak of mutations as of an extraordinary event, more or less contrary to the general movements of life. Exaggerated to a certain degree, they may well appear so. Taken in their essential mechanism, on the other hand, they are an element constantly associated with the generation of living forms. It must not be forgotten that the 'phylogenic' movement presents a very special character. In almost all the other movements that we are in the habit of studying (spatial displacement, physico-chemical transformations, ontogenic evolution . . .) the subject of change forms a continuous basis for the

successive modifications that appear. In the development of a zoo-logical species the case is quite different. Even if the germ-plasm should be regarded as forming an autonomic and physically con-tinuous link between individuals of a single genealogical series, this mysterious stolon would still remain, throughout its life, under the influence of the beings that have transitorily budded on its stem. The movement of the species takes place by leaps from one individual to another. Now what, from the kinetic or dynamic point of view, are these moving things on which movement successively rests? Un-doubtedly, each one of them represents a small independent system, a possibility of morphological deviation. Just as on a plant stem, each leaf (and sometimes even each cell) marks a point of possible bud-ding or bifurcation, so along a zoological line each individual is cap-able of deflecting the movement of vital evolution in a particular direction according to the features that give it its precise and indivi-dual quality. Even in a single and recognizable family, viewed ac-cording to their zoological characteristics, the individuals do not form a straight line, but present a series of indentations or tangents in relation to the ideal curve represented by the species. Each individual is a small creation in itself, a possible new species, a charge that may start a phylum, a morphological 'sideways leap'. So true is this that it would take no great exaggeration of the methods employed by palaeontology for the reconstruction of phyla to reach the con-clusion that a son cannot descend from his own father, on the argu-ment that the variation of characteristics between the one and the other does not occur in an irreversible or continuous manner.

Admitting this, we can see that in the majority of cases individual divergences compensate one another. The buds remain virtual, or do not increase. But if certain disturbances or certain necessities or op-portunities occur in the life of the species opening the way to a change of régime or to the adoption of a new way of life (life in the air or the water, for example), then there may conceivably be pro-duced what the great American anatomist and palaeontologist W. K. Gregory calls 'a revolutionary change': a balanced recasting of the organism. Individual possibilities are revealed, the bud bursts and grows, a new branch is actually born on the hitherto hardly supple stem of the ancient phylum.

A revolutionary change, we have said, a recasting. Let us be careful not to exaggerate the extent of the metamorphosis at its beginnings. M. Vialleton very skilfully (though not perversely) devotes himself in this book, to the study of those notoriously very isolated types which, by general admission, attained a paroxysm of specialization. The sudden formation of a present-day bat or seal from an animal resembling a shrew or an otter is clearly unimaginable. But things cannot have happened like this. M. Vialleton points out with some justice that the oldest known equid, the Eocene *Hyracotherium* is already completely a horse in the lightness of his carriage and his general skeletal pattern. This is true. What an admirable attenuated sketch for a horse! Four fore-toes, three hind-toes, short, closely set, low-crowned teeth, etc. etc. . . . Let us carry our thoughts back beyond the *Hyracotherium* by only half the distance that separates him from the modern horse. In my opinion, we still find an animal constructed according to the essential equidian formula. But in this case its 'horselike' characteristics are so inchoate, so hidden that in acquiring them it does not seem to have undergone much more than the organic recasting that accompanies the birth of any living individuality. Observed at this point, the birth of the equids seems no more extraordinary, morphologically speaking, than the appearance of a mere zoological variation. Only our present-day knowledge of the success awaiting this variation allows us to distinguish it from many others. The same applies to the bat and the seal. The first representatives of these two groups had certainly no features as pronounced as their present-day descendants. But, if they had already in germ all the characteristics of the *Chiroptera* and the pinnipeds, it must be, on the evidence of the *Hyracotherium*, in so roughly sketched and concealed a manner that their morphological peculiarities would only have been discernible by a contemporary observer endowed with a marvellous gift of foresight.

2. How is it now that these roughly indicated, and attenuated forms, which are the most interesting to science are always just those

forms that are missing from our collections? By what fatality do the stages which would give us the most certain proof of a vital movement always disappear from our series?

At this point we must introduce a very humble and most accidental factor – a factor so accidental that it might seem to have been arbitrarily invented by transformists on the defensive, if the continual experience of all palaeontologists were not there to guarantee its very tiresome reality; I mean the *automatic destruction of the peduncle of zoological phyla*, a destruction due to two causes: the very small size of beings at the level on which these great morphological changes take place, and in addition the relatively small number of individuals composing living species at their origin.

For a long time[1] it has been observed that the first known representatives of the various zoological families are much smaller than their descendants. The *Hyracotherium* is the size of a fox. The first ruminants are smaller than a hare. The small primates of the lower Eocene are the size of a shrew. The law appears absolutely general. Without pausing to inquire whether the absolute smallness of an animal is not, for some curious reason, a necessary condition of its potential capacity for mutation, let us merely note that the often tiny dimensions of primitive zoological types are a very great obstacle, first to their fossilization and then to their discovery. If the great mammalian dispersion, for example, took place in a group of animals whose average size was that of a mouse, we have very little chance of discovering its traces, unless we presume that the number of mutated individuals was immediately very large. Now, this last point, to which we shall soon return, is very improbable.

M. Vialleton seems to believe that there is a tendency to exaggerate the gaps in our palaeontological knowledge. All that I have learnt from the practice of geology persuades me to the contrary. I would go much further and say that these gaps are so large that it requires a real effort of the imagination even to conceive of their hugeness. In stratigraphy – continental stratigraphy in particular – the 'blanks' are

[1] See for example what M. Depéret has written in his *Transformations du Monde animal*. (Transformations of the animal world).

impressive; more terrains are unknown than are known to us. Palaeontologically our case is still more unfavourable. Even when, for a given epoch, the geological beds exist and are fossil-bearing (which is far from being the general case) we have to admit that we possess only a very poor idea of the animal forms that then peopled the earth. A direct proof of this deficiency in our vision of the past is already provided by the fact that we have only to approach a new region of the world to discover new zoological forms: in palaeontology we never cease to find new things. Other facts are still more significant. There are cases – that of man and the ostriches, for example – in which thanks to the indestructible stone tools abandoned by the former and the very hard eggs left by the latter, we can form some idea of the proportion existing between the number of fossils found and the number of creatures who actually existed. The proportion is unbelievably small. One epoch (the Chellean) yields at most two human bone remains, though its flaked stones are widespread. For the millions of *Struthiolithus* remains that litter the red clays and loess of China, we only possess two or three bones of the bird that laid them. In the same country, the tiger lived during the whole of historical times: I have only heard of one bone that has been found lying on the old soil levels. What does all this mean? Quite simply, that palaeontology (like all long-distance vision) only reveals *maxima*. Before an animal form *begins* to appear in the fossil state, it has to be already legion.[1]

Let us now return to the consideration of phyla and their origin. By all sorts of positive reasons and analogies we are led to think that the formation of zoological species takes a relatively short time. The period being brief, and the mutations no doubt affecting, at the be-

[1] M. L. Cuénot, a specialist in questions of transformism, has kindly informed me that he has for a long time been of this opinion. 'We only know a form,' he writes to me, 'when it has specialized, that is to say when its individuals are numerous and have filled a vacant space in nature. Darwin was of the opposite opinion; he saw in the great species the material of evolution. This idea is absolutely contradicted by the facts. On the contrary, the little species, poor in numbers but endowed with the power of evolution, appear to us to possess a quality the specialized species have lost . . .'

ginnings of each new species, only a relatively small number of re-presentatives of the old species, the absolute quantity of individuals of a truly 'transitional' type is extremely small. Not only is the size of these individuals, who are of such supreme interest to zoology (as we have seen), very slight, but their total number remains perforce extremely small also. In all their quantitative characteristics, the peduncles of phyla therefore stand as *minima* in biological evolution. By virtue of what we know about the difficulties of fossil preservation, they are consequently condemned to disappear. We have no more chance of finding the very earliest Tertiary representatives of equids or simians than the ancestors of the trilobites or worms buried in metamorphic terrains. For different reasons the destruction of both is just as remorselessly certain. Once a phylum becomes per-ceptible to us, it cannot fail to be already entirely defined in its features and hardened in its characteristics. And this explains the paradoxical form in which life presents itself to our eyes: it is like a magnificent tree whose regularly placed and fully grown branches appear to hang from an invisible or imaginary trunk.

3. It may have been noticed that in the preceding explanations one point remains obscure. To account for the oscillations and bifurcations of phyla, we have made use of the phenomenon of mutations. Is not this a purely verbal solution? Does not the whole difficulty of transformism lie precisely in this obscure notion of sudden change, which appears artificially to associate the ideas of stability and movement, of chance and final purpose? However small we suppose the individual variations from which the equidian or chiropteran branch have sprung as side shoots, these variations (as M. Vialleton rightly argues) must have been wonderfully measured, balanced and co-ordinated; otherwise they would not have launched life in such victorious directions. How can we place a blind and chance organic action at the origin of such a harmonious recasting of organs? The moment has come to make ourselves clear on this fundamental point.

What, in my opinion, makes it so difficult for present-day natural scientists to understand and accept mutations is that out of fear of an ill-understood vitalism, they wrongly exclude from their theories the 'plasmatic' role of the living psyche; they wrongly identify 'natural' and 'mechanical'.

This identification and exclusion contradict experience. For we have only to look at the evolution of living beings to perceive that the sequence of their osteological metamorphoses is only the external veil, the façade for the development of an instinct. And they are also unjustified in theory because one could dispense with them without in any way falling into the errors for which the school of Montpellier was once famous. What is unscientific in vitalism is to *intercalate* life in the series of physio-chemical causes in such a way as to make it *directly* produce ponderable or measurable effects which would be peculiar to it – as if it were a kind of radiation or electricity. But if life is conceived (as all spiritual causes should be) as a synthetic force of a higher order than that of the physico-chemical forces, capable of co-ordinating them and acting on them without ever destroying or falsifying their determinisms, then one cannot see why science should blind itself to them any more than to human freedom, with which one cannot think of dispensing unless one is a double-dyed mechanist. Because life is a physical factor *of a higher order* than measurable forces, it is quite as possible to analyse its productions without meeting the thing itself as to explain a watch mechanically without thinking of the watchmaker: at every instant the universe, even if we assume it to possess psychic forces, takes the form of a closed circuit of determinisms which mutually induce one another. But on the other hand, because these psychic forces constitute the co-ordinating factor of various determined systems the totality of which forms the animate world, the successive transformations of this world cannot possibly be explained without recourse to some imponderable forces of synthesis.

This being so, the best way of understanding what goes on in a phylum at the moment of its birth is – in my opinion – I am borrowing the idea from M. Edouard Le Roy – to think of an invention. An instinctive invention, of course, neither analysed nor calculated by its authors. But an invention all the same, or, what comes to the same thing, the awakening and translation into an organism of a desire and a potentiality. There is no reason why certain phyla (burrowing animals or burrow dwellers) should not owe their origin to some anomaly or organic fault, put to use. Nevertheless, in most cases, it is a positive force that seems to be working for the differentiation of life. Is it not, one would ask, a sort of attraction or anticipation of a capacity that launched terrestrial animals into the waters or the air, that sharpened claws or lightened hoofs. When we see to our astonishment, teeth becoming reduced and sharper along the phylum of the carnivores (that is to say, alterations in the organs best constructed by their rigidity to escape the modifications resulting from usage), how can we avoid thinking of the accentuation of a temperament or a passion, that is to say of the development of a moral character rather than the evolution of an anatomical one? If we do so, immediately the perfect correlation of the various organic modifications at the moment of a mutation no longer seems in the least extraordinary. If it is no longer an isolated morphological element that is changing, but the very centre of co-ordination of all the organs that is shifting, the creature can only transform itself harmoniously and as a whole.

This, I repeat, is in no way a return to the vital forces and 'virtues' of bad scholasticism. Less and less will the conscientious scientist be able to dispense with a precise analysis of the determinisms utilized and grouped by life in its effort to externalize the tendencies which are, indubitably, its most consistent reality. But unless he resolves at the same time to view these tendencies as the final empirical source of the evolutionary energies he is studying, the organic transformations of the animal world will be as inexplicable to him as the historical adventures of human society to a purely determinist historian. The transformist paradox will block his way as an insoluble difficulty.

Would not such a concession to spiritual ideas seem to him the equivalent of destroying the very idea of evolution? To admit the role of a formative psyche in the formation of species looks to him like a denial of transformism. M. Vialleton writes in this way because for some reason I do not understand, he identifies transformism and mechanism. I find it impossible to accept the reality of the dilemma with which our opponents claim to face us. To be a transformist, as I have often said, is not to be a Darwinian or a Lamarckian or the disciple of any particular school. It is quite simply to admit that the appearance of living creatures on earth obeys an ascertainable law, whatever that law may be. Neither mutationism nor vitalism properly understood conflicts with this attitude.

c   Conclusion

The preceding reflections will, I hope, have shown that without resorting to any essentially new factor of zoological metamorphosis, and on the sole condition of not excluding the wisely localized intervention of vital forces, it is possible to explain in transformist terms the discontinuities, at first sight so disconcerting, of animal evolution.

We should, however, be concealing the basis of our thought, were we not to add in conclusion the following observations.

Hitherto in the study of life, as in that of matter, scientists have primarily tried to find the reason for phenomena in the action of elementary causes. It would seem that the stellar world can only be explained by corpuscular forces, and the living world by individual actions. One may wonder whether this kind of atomism, despite its undeniable advantages, will suffice for much longer for the task of making reality scientifically comprehensible. Beside the properties resulting from collective play of the parts, there must also be in every organized whole certain other properties, measurable or not, belonging to the collectivity as such, which neither the analysis nor the sum of the elementary forces could ever account for. Can we really claim to explain the world without giving these latter a greater part of our attention; that is to say, without envisaging the existence and without investigating the specific attributes of natural unities larger than those to which we habitually confine our studies?

Terrestrial life stands in the forefront of those vast entities which invite us to study them directly. Were we to do so, many difficulties would probably vanish which remain insuperable so long as all we examine in the world is its elementary energies. Appearing in close dependence on the physico-chemical conditions of our planet, life represents in its productions an important and inseparable part of our cosmic unity. Questions of metaphysical pride apart, there is no more reason for divorcing plants and animals from the earth, than granite or the sea waters. But if, because rooted and isolated on the same planet, life forms a solid, unified and patterned mass, this mass, as such, must show itself in currents, oscillations and laws which are characteristic not of a certain individual life or of life in general, but of terrestrial life considered as forming a specific whole.

We have already pointed out the curious properties of plasticity and differentiation that appear in a fauna as soon as it is geographically isolated. In such a group, a certain balance progressively establishes itself between herbivorous, carnivorous, burrowing and other types, as if any large enough fragment of life – taken as a cutting, as one might say – tended to reproduce as a stem the general design of the tree from which it has been taken. Do not these facts point to an autonomous power of organization and differentiation, in no way localized in individuals, but diffused in any large portion of animate matter?

Another indication. We have already tried to interpret the sudden appearance and linear development of zoological characteristics in terms of individual psychic intentions or tendencies. But we have not ventured to explain how it happens that these mutations declare themselves simultaneously in a relatively large number of individuals who suddenly begin to drift simultaneously in the same direction.

A final, still more significant indication. If we observe biological evolution in its broad outlines, we see to our surprise that each new blossoming of superior forms reduces the pressure of the sap in the lower branches. There seems to be a certain constancy, a certain invariance in the total quantity of energy carried by terrestrial life. Does not this unity of growth between the various realms of the organic world show that there is some actual physical unity informing the whole?

Indeed, if we put these various symptoms and others like them together, we begin seriously to envisage the possible existence of a vast living telluric entity, difficult to describe (since it is of a higher order of magnitude than ours and we are engulfed in it), but the seat of perfectly definite physical qualities. And in this mysterious but not metaphorical biosphere, we seem capable of finding answers to many questions that have remained unanswered all round us. Is it not here that we must now place the seat, the spring, the ultimate regulator of zoological evolution? Who knows (and here I adopt an idea that does not appear alien to M. Vialleton's views) – who knows if the final solution of the transformist paradox does not lie in the conception of a universe in which the principal zoological types, as distinct from one another as the rays of a light spectrum, would find their connection in the fact that they radiate from a common force of organic development, whose seat is the world as a whole?

What is plastic in the world of living creatures, what moves, what periodically divides into newly formed branches, will in this case not be the elements (which are confined to small-scale variations) but the physical power that envelops all these elements.

These views, being still extremely confused, are awkward to express. At first sight they look strange, almost fantastic. We cannot yet see either how they could lead to useful experiments. I have, however, felt it necessary to present them in order to show how limitlessly the world is expanding under scientific research, and that the idea of transformism is progressively escaping the narrow boundaries in which its adversaries would like to confine it.

For it is extremely curious to observe (and with this remark I will end) that, if the new perspectives of discontinuity and polyphyletism, which we have just paused to consider, should assume substance, the old evolutionary ideas of the nineteenth century, far from vanishing like a mirage, would on the contrary attain their true expression.

The more one studies the history of the transformist movement, the more convinced one is that, like all other great enlightenments of human thought, it is only gradually becoming conscious of its own implications. It has been successively considered that the essence of transformism is the adaptation of living forms to their surroundings and the inheritance of acquired characteristics, or perhaps natural selection, or perhaps monophyletism, or at least the theory of descent. It now appears that underlying these particular explanations, a much more general and profound idea is coming to light: that of a certain physical 'immanence' (forgive the philosophical term) in life.

The theory that today prevails in our scientific representations of the world is that nothing enters into the field of our physical experience that is not materially dependent on pre-existent elements. Formerly we were not too surprised by the sudden addition of an atom to the cosmic mass, or by its sudden displacement across space. Today we no longer doubt that the existence of a molecule of hydrogen, for example, and its localization at a given point in the universe has required the immensity of a whole astral evolution. If it is to be reducible to scientific thought, everything must extend its empirical roots indefinitely backwards and in all directions: this is the postulate which we find at the basis of all modern scientific research, but which the majority of scientists do not even think of proclaiming, so evident does it seem to them and so habitual has it become. To extend this postulate to life, that is the real business of the new transformism.

Contemporary transformism cares very little about the number of animal phyla, and finds the divisions between them unimportant. Only one thing would upset it: that any one of these phyla, traced to its origins, should not be continued by something further back; that a single one of these discontinuities should not, in its existence and magnitude, obey ascertainable physical conditions. *Understood in the beginning principally as a need for change, evolution has become principally a law of birth,* and the acceptance of this law appears to be final.

For this reason, though natural scientists, under pressure of the transformist paradox, give greater importance in their theories to the fixed and the discontinuous, anti-evolutionists would be quite wrong in imagining that we are returning to the old 'fixed type' thought. If living creatures seem to us today more independent of one another than Lamarck, Darwin or Gaudry thought, they have on the other hand become much more closely united to the world that bears them. And by this fact, if one takes a fundamental view, the attitude of all modern zoologists and biologists (even of M. Vialleton, as can be seen by his method of work) is that of an ultra-transformism. We have never been further than we are now from the ancient creationism[1] that represented creatures as appearing ready made in surroundings which received them with indifference. Ideas, like life of which they are the highest manifestation, never turn back.

Revue des questions scientifiques, January 1925.

[1] Is it necessary to recall that far from being incompatible with the existence of a Primal Cause, transformist views, as set out here, present its influx in the noblest and most heartening manner possible? For the Christian transformist, God's creative action is no longer conceived as an intrusive thrusting of His works into the midst of pre-existent beings, but as a *bringing to birth* of the successive stages of His work in the heart of things. It is no less essential, no less universal, no less intimate either on that account.

CHAPTER VI

THE NATURAL HISTORY OF THE WORLD
REFLEXIONS ON THE VALUE AND FUTURE OF SYSTEMATICS

Systematics seems to be a very modest and very aged branch of the tree of the sciences. The very name recalls the venerable and heroic times of Linnaeus and Buffon – the age when any study of life could be made a matter of collecting and labelling – the age when all knowledge of the organic world was described in natural history.

It is not useless, I assure you, to react against the tendency to compare the efforts of classifiers disadvantageously with researches considered nobler, higher, more penetrating, such as anatomy, physiology, cytology, biochemistry and many others that explore living matter with greatly improved methods and techniques.

The purpose of these lines is to show – without paradox, we hope – that the classifying activity of natural scientists, as today understood:

(1) has not only become as exalted a task as any other scientific analysis of reality;

(2) is on the way to discovering for itself and opening to the other sciences concerned with nature a new realm of research;

(3) that its object, however (the natural distribution of beings) is gradually being found to be the common and supreme end to which all human scientific effort, on its speculative side, converges.

A. *True Nature of Present-Day Systematics: A Generalized Anatomy and Physiology*

To know a thing (whether being or phenomenon) scientifically, is to place it in a physical system of temporal antecedents and spatial links.

For so long, therefore, as living forms were considered fixed unities, juxtaposed (however harmoniously and 'naturally') by the *extrinsic* operation of an intelligence, there was no other method of understanding them intellectually than to describe and arrange them in logical divisions supposedly corresponding to those of the creative idea. Until the appearance of the evolutionary point of view, natural history was not (could not be) true science. Quite the reverse. From the moment when ideas of birth and becoming began to throw light on the ideas which the natural scientists were forming of animal and vegetable species, systematic zoology and botany became part of the block already formed by anatomy, physics, chemistry and astronomy. One need only have performed the modern task of classification for a short time to be convinced that the fusion between the different disciplines has during the last century become closer every day.

It is clearly impossible to guess what will happen to the transformist theory in the future. Our successors will probably find our present conceptions of vital evolution very childish and make great corrections. Already today, however, one thing appears certain: whatever new facets may be added to our theories by future progress the biological sciences will increasingly stress the views of the physical and organic interdependence of living forms that Lamarck and Darwin translated, knowing no better, into terms of simple generation, adaptation and heredity. In the realm of life, as in that of matter, the fundamental unity of the universe and the inexorable interrelationship of the cosmic elements, which will only allow any new being to enter our experience in the context of all the present and past states of the world known to science,[1] appear to be ideas now definitely accepted by the human mind. We shall never abandon them again, but explore them, on the contrary, to increasing depth because we have been both drawn and driven to them by the full force of human thought for many centuries; and also because, once they are accepted, reality is found to grow clearer and more orderly so far as the eye can see.

In view of this fact, what has become and what will increasingly

[1] This is not a law of determinism, be it noted, but a law of *birth*.

become of the work of classification? What is meant today by defining a living form? Is it simply as it was of old, to find it a place in a dichotomic picture? Evidently not, no one believes in that any longer. For a natural scientist worthy of the name, to class an animal or vegetable is to find it its true, natural place in the organized assembly of living forms, considered as a whole in process of development. To understand a being, therefore, it is no longer enough to have enumerated its characteristics, or by reference to one or other of its characteristics (the most apparent or the most convenient) to have added it to one or another division of a catalogue. The labour must be much more exhaustive. It is necessary (at least approximately and provisionally) to have reconstituted its organic history, explained its biological surroundings, and accounted for its geographical distribution. Just as the branch of a tree (however recognizable in itself by its form and features) can only be physically defined by the year of its growth, the height at which it appeared on the parent trunk, its numerical place among the sub-divisions of the principal stem, the links by which it is attached to such and such a neighbouring bough; so no living species seems any longer understandable except by the place it holds by birth in the whole edifice of organized forms. Good generic or specific characteristics are precisely those which best reveal this situation.

It matters little here whether the different natural groups appearing on the tree of life are comparable on the one hand to the leaves of a plant (organs more or less homogeneous with the stem that bears them) or on the other to independent calyces budding on the axis of a polypary. Whether there is continuity or discontinuity at the root of species; whether the various types of organisms form a series with no other breaks but those between individuals, or whether they are divisible into a finite number of closed specific combinations (analogous to bodies in chemistry), the fact remains – and here classical transformists and mutationists are in agreement – that no living form 'hangs in the air'. Each is attached by some part of itself to a pre-existent prototype, to a morphological antecedent – and each is connected also with its neighbouring forms. This is in itself sufficient to raise the science of classification to an equality with the great sciences of life.

If everything is actually connected in the realm of animal and plant forms, what difference is there between the work of the classifier and that of the other biologists? From the point of view of essential method, none.

When the classifying zoologist, for example, in order to define a dog or a lizard, tries to distinguish and reconstitute the phyla of these animals, he is acting (though with other means and a different scale of magnitudes) exactly like the anatomist who, in order to recognize the scientific nature of a heart, a skull, a nerve (objects eminently describable in themselves, nevertheless) finds himself obliged to dissect the organisms in different stages of their development, and to practise histology or embryogeny.

Again, when this same zoologist, in order to account for the appearance and modifications of certain morphological apparatus (limbs, wings, teeth, etc.) makes it his business to discover the biological conditions in which the amphibians, birds or mammals, for example, were formed, or is perhaps led to presume a sort of balance, within a single group, between carnivores, herbivores, climbers and burrowers, etc., his work is exactly parallel to that of the physiologist who, putting aside the hereditary anatomical characteristics of a living being, tries to define it as a viable association of functions. When this zoologist, in fact, in order to imagine an origin for his phyla (that is to say in order to glimpse a solution to the irritating problems of the origin of life on earth and the differentiation between the kingdoms or branches of the organic world) suspects that he must have recourse to the idea that life and its greater mutations are a function of the physico-chemical conditions regulating the *astral* evolution of the earth conceived as a specific whole (in the same way as a chemical molecule) *then* not only does he discover an immense extension of biochemistry stretching ahead of him, but rejoins the realm of geochemistry, which is already being explored.

The only important fundamental difference between systematics on the one hand, and the other biological sciences, on the other, is that the latter confine themselves to the study of organic unities which are found to be of the same order as our human individuality, while the former dissects the elements and balances the functions of an indefinitely larger organized mass, that is to say the layer of life enveloping the earth, the 'Biosphere' (Suess): an immense object, which only seems vague to us because we are immersed in it as in the Milky Way, but a magnificent object which systematics, to its very great glory, has helped to reveal and analyse.

B. *A New Realm Opened by Systematics: The Biosphere*

To the great good fortune of systematics, setting out to make certain logical divisions in which to arrange living creatures, and finding instead organic links which proved increasingly numerous and general, it has ended by discovering a physical reality of a higher order without which these links would be inexplicable. One fine day, confronted by the flexible and orderly results to which its classifications led it, 'positional' biology saw that above living creatures there exists life: not, of course, a universal organism of which living beings must be elements, but a physical reality of a separate order, scientfically characterized by perfectly determined specific qualities. From that moment it possessed the right material to study and could fulfil the purpose for which it was born.

A certain number of the qualities that reveal and characterize the natural unity of the living terrestrial mass are merely repetitions on a larger scale of those belonging to the individual living being (vegetable or animal). Such are:[1] the subdivision of groups (orders, families, kinds, geographically isolated fauna, etc.) in regular verticils, conforming to a fixed number of principal lines (tree-dwellers, runners, flyers, burrowers, swimmers, insectivores, carnivores, herbivores, etc.); the power that compels certain lines indefinitely to increase the accentuation of a characteristic, to 'grow' unceasingly (orthogenesis), while others remained imperturbably fixed in their

[1] To say nothing of the monocellular origin of beings, and the general laws of propagation, the discovery of which is not due to systematics in particular.

characteristics; the aptitude of a group to produce abundant new forms, or on the contrary, its complete sterility; the general tendency of all phyla, great and small, to attain a higher psychism: all signs of growth, in a word, proving that zoological groups as well as individuals pass through a phase of plasticity, differentiation and fecundity, afterwards to become fixed and die.

These various phenomena which charm us by their breadth without disconcerting us by their novelty, are well known; and they have for long led to discussions (though too metaphorically and cautiously perhaps) of the life of the species, that is to say, in short, of the life of the whole group of living beings. We should no doubt connect with them, by way of specific properties of terrestrial life (considered as a natural whole) a series of other facts, also brought to light by systematics, facts which at a first meeting disconcert the biologist, since they present no exact analogy with any phenomenon of life in the field of experience. We refer to the phenomena of sudden appearance which must have marked the first blossoming of life on earth, and which seem to reproduce themselves periodically each time a really new organized type adds itself to the vegetable or animal series.[1] This category of events still seems extremely mysterious. But cannot this mystery be ascribed to the fact that, in order to interpret them, we must find their roots not in the particular organisms (in the living individuals) but in the organisms taken collectively (in life taken all together)?

We have already touched on this important question. But we must now return to it. Hitherto biologists have chiefly concerned themselves with explaining the history of life on the basis of the elementary factors of evolution (that is to say individuals). In doing so, have they not committed the same mistake as those who try to understand an animal's organs without allowing for the power of heredity

[1] In a recent book, *Membres et ceintures des Vertébrés tétrapodes*, Paris, 1923, M. Vialleton, the eminent professor at Montpellier, has most cogently presented the reasons compelling us to admit that organic evolution took place by leaps, by a succession of brusquely recast organisms rather than by partial and gradual modifications.

and co-ordination which is characteristic of the whole animal? It is very difficult to give a clear form to intuitions that are still vague, to simple presentiments. We begin to suspect one, however: just as the phenomena of 'radiative' adaptation are probably a function of the general equilibrium of living groups considered as forming a single physiological block; so we presume that life's inventions are, at least in part, an effect of large numbers, that is to say the result of an infinity of constantly repeated attempts to find a biological way forward towards more-being or better-being (an attempt whose resultant might be compared to the pressure exercised by a gas on a container): so sudden appearances or mutations (if they take place) are very likely to find their empirical explanation in some supra-individual and unitary maturing of the protoplasma (the Neo-Darwinists' 'germ'), a maturing linked with the global constitution and evolution of the telluric unity. Considered in its beginnings and in its principal lines of direction, life will not start to become scientifically comprehensible until the physico-chemical history of the planet of which it is the conscious envelope has been deciphered. If these still very dim perspectives were to become sharp, clearly systematics, by revealing the breaks at which the direct influence of the biosphere manifests itself – dominating individual causes by right of privilege – would have opened a huge new realm to the biological sciences.

Henceforth we can affirm, on the sole strength of the indications we have just noted, that systematics strongly supports the sciences of the inorganic world in their tendency to approach the problems of matter with a new sense of the breadth and connections of phenomena, that is to say from an increasingly cosmic point of view. Thanks to spectral analysis and the radiant substances, physical chemistry is already far advanced in its study of the evolution of the basic material of the universe. Now geology, in its turn, is led to a conception of phenomena (folds, overthrusts, distribution of continents, etc) which can have no equivalent among elementary material phenomena; that is to say, which are irreducible to the modes of action of any material unity of a lesser order of magnitude than the earth. The science of the earth, we feel, will only deserve the name when, neglecting the secondary effects which can be reproduced in the laboratory, it has discerned and isolated the group of specifically terrestrial effects characterizing the unity earth (as other properties characterize the unity hydrogen or the unity sun). At that moment biology, geology and astronomy will have come very close together, and we shall discover, no doubt to our great astonishment, that the roots of sociology also lie very deep in this same block.

Indeed science appears to be reaching the age at which, having occupied itself principally with elementary magnitudes, it will now attempt a direct approach to the study of cosmic movements and unities. If this tendency becomes sharper, systematics, still the only science explicitly to explore the biosphere, will no doubt see the field of its researches broken up and subdivided. It will perhaps give place one day to an anatomy, physiology and biochemistry of life in general. These sciences, whose combined functions it now exercises, will individualize at its expense. Even so it will retain the honour not only of having opened the way towards new perspectives, but of having also provided the model and furnished the nucleus for findings that the combined efforts of all the speculative sciences must strain to realize.

c. *Systematics, the Speculative Goal of all Science*

Philosophers who have been analysing the value of science for thirty years have very strongly insisted on the relative and provisional character of human knowledge, especially in physics. They have revealed the simplifications, approximations, interpretations of all sorts that concrete nature, the 'fact', has undergone when submitted to our mathematical laws. They have assessed the precarious life of hypotheses. One might almost think, as one reads them, that capable though science is in its practical mastery of material energies, it is powerless when it comes to the question of extending our perception of reality and constructing a gradually more intelligible universe.

There is a measure of exaggeration in these criticisms, which is immediately evident as soon as one distinguishes the two very different elements in scientific constructions: (*a*) mathematical expressions relating measures applied to phenomena; and (*b*) the physical entities (properties, in the first place but afterwards the natural cores) progressively discerned and discovered by a network of laws and calculations.

The first of these two elements is undoubtedly very relative. The mathematical representation of physical realities depends on the point of view chosen by the modern physicist (and by the whole of physics for at least the last two centuries), by his method of approaching nature and dividing up phenomena. It varies, according to the precision of procedures. It is constantly submitted to a sort of idealization. Mathematical laws in fact, are a language which could vary greatly from its present form and still describe the same things as it does today.

The same is not true of the physical entities which provide the material basis for mathematical constructions. This second element in scientific theory has in fact an absolute value; it represents a true and definite invariable, that is to say something which once discovered is destined to remain the same under all investigations and analyses, in all languages and from all points of view.

Let us take the typical case of the discovery of Neptune. The astronomical laws which Le Verrier used for his calculations were only approximate. The progress of astronomy and mathematics will perhaps modify them very profoundly. They sufficed, however, for the discovery of an unknown celestial body. This new planet was a definite achievement by science.

Let us now take the more modern case of atoms and electrons. For some years, the study of radiations led scientists to suspect the existence of extremely small centres of matter, the objective reality of which, confirming that of the particles imagined by chemistry, tends to impose itself on science as an actual fact. Clearly, the mathematical laws regulating the distribution and movement of electrons are liable to great changes. But the electrons themselves, once 'seen' (directly), as they very soon will be, will no more depart from the heaven of human experience than Neptune, once seen through a telescope, or the sun. There will be new ways of viewing, combining and understanding them. But they will always be there.

In crystallography also, although the physical laws of symmetry are still very approximate, the Haüy networks are, thanks to the X-ray, in process of taking objective form.

By assembling these facts and others like them, we soon perceive that the most solid part, the truly indestructible residue of the conquests of science, in physics and chemistry, is represented by the discovery and cataloguing of a vast family of natural unities, centres, nuclei,[1] defined by specific properties and grouped in graded categories. These nuclei are too small, too numerous, for us to be able yet (or indeed ever) to characterize them individually, which we should have to do in order to know them as well as we know animals. Perhaps, however, we shall come to discern distinctions and races among them (carbon races, albumin races, why not?). In any case science already understands that it will attain no intellectual mastery of the atomic groups till it comes to know not only the length of their life but the long sequence of their sidereal evolution also.

What conclusion can we reach except that physics, chemistry and astronomy are contributing their most valuable speculative results to a purpose, required by both nature and truth; that here, before our eyes, they are jointly constructing a vast systemics of the inorganic world into which the classification of organic beings can be inserted on the level of the biosphere? The tree of inorganic unities (atomic and sidereal) is beginning to envelop and relay with its branches the tree of organic unities. Little by little, systematic bio-

---

[1] It will be noticed that during a first phase (Neptune before its discovery by telescope, electrons before the convergent results of the last experiments, etc.) these natural nuclei have been simply 'hypotheses'. This shows how unfair it is always to describe a hypothesis as a provisional and transitory means of arranging our knowledge. Far from being a scientific accessory, hypothesis is the aim, the soul, and true content of scientific theory; it is like life, changeable, fragile but progressive. Good hypotheses are continually modified but in a definite direction, which they perfect themselves by following; and at the end of this evolution they attain the rank of fixed elements, destined to figure thereafter in any representation of the world.

logy, that is to say the science of living unities seen in their hierarchies and history, is penetrating and assimilating what were considered the noblest sciences, those most apt to be governed by formulae and figures.

The old systematics would patently be wrong to pride itself on these conquests (or at least on that influence). Its realm, the world of living beings, formed of perfectly distinct and clearly seriated parts was an ideal field for the simple discovery of the value of natural orders and the enormous importance of evolution in the world. It earned no great merit by being the first to direct its researches along lines that proved to be the right ones. Nevertheless, its detractors have done wrong to despise it.

It is undoubtedly a great glory for the 'naturalists' that, encouraged by the discovery that there are physical relations of antecedence between living forms, the modest series of Buffon and Linnaeus have multiplied and amplified their ramifications till they embrace the whole cosmos: to such good purpose that if we had to find a general name for speculative science, in the form that the alliance of the most abstruse and the exact disciplines of our century tends to give it, it would no doubt be best to call it 'the natural history of the world'.

Scientia (Revue Internationale de Synthèse Scientifique), January 1925.

CHAPTER VII

ON THE NECESSARILY DISCONTINUOUS
APPEARANCE OF EVERY EVOLUTIONARY
SERIES

One of the principal objections habitually advanced against transformism is based on the fact that the evolutionary series constructed
by palaeontology, while arranging themselves in a natural order, remain as if suspended in the air, without attachment to a common
trunk: the transitional types between phyla (or, if you prefer it, the
birth of phyla) always remain out of reach. 'No visible intermediates'
say the believers in fixed types, 'therefore no evolution.'

To discover the weakness of this objection, one has only to observe that the appearances of discontinuity and fixity, so constantly
pointed out and discussed in the case of palaeontological reconstructions, are to be found, in exactly the same form, in those scientific
perspectives that we take as indisputably evolutionary; human
civilizations, institutions, languages and ideas for instance. Who
could tell the origin of the Sumerians, Egyptians or Phoenicians? Or
of Hebrew, Greek or Latin? But who would dare to argue that these
languages appeared one day fully formed, without mutual relations
and with no law presiding over their birth?

The truth is that past realities of any kind never leave us anything
but vestiges of themselves corresponding to their quantitative
maxima, that is to say to their period of success and stability. The
periods of birth and establishment, which correspond to minima of
duration and breadth, disappear automatically from our vision,
leaving no trace.

In short, when submitted to scientific investigation, life's past reacts identically with all other pasts. Far therefore from proving that

the animal world forms an exceptional realm, refractory to history, the discontinuity of phyletic series is a positive indication of the reality of a biological evolution as easily recognizable as that of the Roman Empire.

L'Anthropologie, vol. XXXVI. Contribution by Pierre Teilhard de Chardin to the Société d'Anthropologie, at a meeting on March 17, 1926.

CHAPTER VIII

THE BASIS AND FOUNDATIONS OF THE IDEA OF EVOLUTION

The more one explores for oneself and the more one explains to others the perspectives of biological evolutionism, the more surprised one is at their simplicity and breadth, and at the evidence for them; and the more astonished one is also that their adversaries are so slow in putting aside marginal or ill-conceived questions in order to look carefully at either the problems or the basic answers, which alone deserve examination.

I shall try in the course of these pages to isolate once more what we may call the essence of transformism, that is to say the group of facts, views and attitudes which constitute the basis and foundations of the evolutionary idea; and I propose to show that, reduced to these essentials (whatever name one then gives them) transformism is so mixed up with the mass of tendencies and notions characteristic of modern science and consciousness that we must see it not only as a definite advance but also an inevitable form of human thought to which unsuspectingly the most determined believers in fixed types are the first to submit.

A. *The Structure of the Living World and the Fundamental Condition of Evolution*

The most general proof (one might say the one and inexhaustible proof) of an evolution of organic matter must be sought in the undeniable traces of structure which the world of life considered as a whole manifests on analysis.

As a result of the very natural habit which causes us to measure things by the scale of our bodies, the idea and understanding of pluri- or supra-individual organisms are less familiar to us than those of isolated beings. Nevertheless, the existence in nature of vast animate complexes is proved to us by precise phenomena, as indisputable as those characterizing the relation of parts within each separate plant or animal. There is a natural distribution and interlinking of the living elements of the world in time and in space: this is the conclusion, for which ever-increasing evidence is found and to which natural scientists and biologists of all kinds are coming, impelled by the countless branches of this old science called natural history, now in full course of renewal, and also by the other disciplines, still anonymous or disguised under childish names (botanical geography, bio-geography, chemistry or sociology of living groups . . .) whose slow convergence has prepared the way for a science of the biosphere.[1]

Clearly we cannot think of deploying this great mass of evidence here. We will content ourselves by briefly recalling what has often been said about the form that past life is gradually taking for our eyes. There is no longer anyone who denies that from end to end of the immense history that is being reconstituted, point by point, by the continuous efforts of palaeontology, we are discovering the organic – or, if you prefer it, the organization of the organized.

The organic first of all appears in the obvious relations between what is called the purely material world and the layer of terrestrial life taken globally. It is structurally, and not by a sort of adhesion, that organic matter is bound to the very architecture of the earth. Localized in the hydrosphere and atmosphere, that is to say in the zone of water, oxygen and carbon dioxide, it sinks its roots to the

[1] Is it necessary to say that by biosphere we do not mean 'some great animal' the destroyer of individual spontaneity, but merely a natural association of individuals in some unity of a higher order, which can only be imagined by *analogy* with everything else we know about natural unities. The biosphere must inevitably be a reality *sui generis*; and to conceive of it our mind must rise by a positive effort, analogous to the effort which in the case of mathematics, for example, has compelled the acceptance (to the great consternation of Euclidean geometry) of irrational and incommensurable magnitudes side by side with whole numbers.

depths of the geochemical soil produced by the evolution itself of our planet. In the constitution and laws of the cellular elements, we see the great cosmic laws of gravity, capillary attraction, molecular forces, appearing in particular manners by which we can to some extent read the individuality of the earth. The original phases of this connection escape us. But from the moment when geology reveals the first traces of the biosphere, we can follow the extraordinary mingling of two kinds of matter, inorganic and organic; the latter perpetually infiltrating the former in order to alter its chemical cycles and conquer it, physical layer after layer, by a continual synergy (since one dare not yet say symbiosis). From the most microscopic bacteria to the largest group of fauna, life appears to us as constantly interwoven, to its very depths, with the micro- and macro-diastrophisms of the earth. It is often said that palaeontology ought to be divorced from geology and united with zoology. Is it not zoology, on the contrary that should be included in geology, to be treated and understood as a biostratigraphy or bio-geology? This coalescence between life and matter has been recognized for a long time, no doubt from the very beginning. But we are still far from having understood the vast consequences of this fact, which is as simple, as mysterious as the movement of the planets or the distribution of the oceans.

Forming a natural zone (and not a parasitic annex) of our planet, life has a total physiognomy that is not easy to comprehend and that we could not possibly evaluate, having no terms of comparison. In its present distribution, nevertheless, we can at least distinguish some general characteristic expressive, either of an astounding power of expansion and malleability, or of a general ascent towards greater consciousness and freedom. Life fills all fields with its branches, generally terminates them with forms in which the nervous system attains a maximum of complication and concentration. In the general design of the biosphere, considered in so far as is possible from outside and in contrast to simple matter, there is already a most remarkable indication of structure, which will become much clearer to our eyes, if we try to follow it in a more restricted field.

Let us, for the sake of simplicity, leave the infinitely complex universe – which we so naïvely simplify – of unicellular beings: and ignoring even the primitive division of the metazoa into plants, coelenterata, insects, etc. (so many interwoven worlds, whose true 'parallaxes' still escape us), let us observe the present and past division of the vertebrates as it took place.

One first fact immediately strikes us: in this branching out (the most recent department of life, the study of which serves us as a key and a model for the comprehension of all other living groups), the forms we catalogue are disposed in successive layers, each of which in its turn occupies the whole of the biosphere and then more or less completely disappears, to be replaced by the following layer. Certain armoured *Pisciformata* (most improperly confused with fish), amphibians, theromorphs, reptiles, mammals, and one should add, man (more important than a class or even a branch in the bio-geological balance) constitute so many expansions or waves of life over the whole of the globe; expansions each distinct from the other, but despite the discontinuities, to which we shall return at some length, obeying an undeniable law of distribution. However limited our perspectives by the shortness of explorable time, we can see the bio-sphere renewing itself at least six times in the zoological realm to which we are confining ourselves. This means at least six vital pulsations of the first order on the axis of vertebrate life.

Let us apply ourselves to the study of one of these pulsations in isolation. We shall observe that it can be broken down or divided in its turn into quite natural parts, of which the closest to our vision are those resulting from harmonization to a different surrounding (air, water, earth, plants, trees, etc.) of a basic morphological type. In this way a system of lines (the 'radiations' of American writers) is formed in each branch or class, in response to the demands of the surroundings; the verticil of this system, particularly recognizable in the reptiles and mammals (and under so-called 'artificial' forms in man himself) appearing already in the poorer or ill-known groups of the theromorphs and amphibians. In reality the verticils of which we are speaking are very complex. Each fibre of their crowns appears on analysis to be formed of a bundle of parallel rays each connected to one of the increasingly elementary sub-verticils produced by the burgeoning of groups of the second and third order, etc., into which the zoological branches or classes break up.

Thus in the mammals, burrowers may be marsupials, insectivores or rodents; swimmers may be sirenians, cetaceans or carnivores; solipeds may be horses or notungulates (or Tertiary ungulates of South America). But let us provisionally ignore this complication and apply ourselves to the study of a single radiation, as simple as possible, in a single verticil. Let us follow one or another of these lines in time. We shall notice that the zoological type, on the axis chosen, varies regularly by specializing in a fixed direction. This is especially the case in the phyletic lines (horse, camel, elephant, etc.) to which we have for long much too closely limited ourselves, taking their type of curve as the general design of transformations throughout life.

Successive layers within a single general unity, verticils in the layers, phyletic fibres in the verticils: these are the principal types of groupings presented by complex living unities. We must now thoroughly understand this: the law of composition or decomposition which we have discovered, like all laws regulating the molecular structure of a crystal, or the distribution of leaves or branches on a plant, is only a law of recurrence. We have studied it in the case of the larger or medium-sized units of life. But it is possible, in some favourable cases, to follow it much lower (and probably much higher) to the point of recognizing a 'congenital' and structural arrangement of organic matter itself. The better we know an animal group, the more we see it resolving into a growing number of successive fans, each smaller than the last.

It is particularly interesting and easy to make our observations within the human group. Because humanity is at present in full vigour and by its delicate variations of race and culture allows of an infinity of physiological and psychological differentiations, we can successfully identify an infinite number of reduced harmonics beneath the basic pulsation. Man as such divides into fossil men and

Homo sapiens; the latter into whites, yellows and blacks; each of these groups in its turn splits up into all sorts of ethnic units. And we must go yet further; even in the history of each family, in the very development of each individual, or of each idea in the individual, it is possible to recognize, in the nascent state, the mechanism of dispersion, of spreading and relaying that governs the march of the greatest living entities within our field of comprehension. The same work of analysis would clearly be possible in all zoological groups if we knew them, their 'bodies and souls' better.

Let us now leave things considered as such and resume the question in its connections with our labour of scientific research. In this respect, all that we have just said can be summed up in the following statement. There exists the vast science of systematics pursued for more than a century by a growing number of researchers in ever-increasing detail and in constantly expanding fields. This science, whose initial purpose was to establish a simple nominal or logical classification of beings, has under the pressure of facts gradually become a veritable anatomy or histology of the layer of life on earth. Not only has it assumed this new form, thus showing its possibilities; but it continues to grow stronger and spread. Beneath its analytical researches, the biosphere breaks up so far as our vision extends, into great and small, and finally forms only an immense natural network of elements, lying alongside and covering one another. In this network, once it is established, each newly discovered living form takes an effortless place, which completes the continuity of the whole. Well, this is a very remarkable achievement, and it is strange that we have been so long in recognizing its cause. *Everything is classified; therefore everything holds together.* In fact it is not the simple evidence of a few isolated or fugitive facts, but the whole life of a flourishing discipline (that is to say the day-to-day control of observations repeated by the thousand) that vouches for it: the gigantic mass formed by the totality of living beings is no chance association or accidental juxtaposition; it constitutes a natural grouping, that is to say a physically organized unity.

Having reached this point in our inquiry, we have only one more step to make, and we shall see revealed before us in all its breadth the fundamental and inexhaustible truth of transformism that we postulated at the beginning of this section. The biosphere, as we have just observed, presents itself as a *constructed whole*, the external structure of great adjusted blocks being repeated by an internal texture of smaller elements. One conclusion is inevitable; that it took shape progressively. Alter things and words as we may, so far we have found only one way of explaining the structure of the world of life discovered by systematics; we can see it only as the result of a development, of an 'evolution'. Life in its major branches as in its most delicate derivatives bears the manifest traces of a germination and growth. On this essential point we must recognize the state of mind that modern science has now definitely reached. Let us set down the truth; it would be easier to persuade a botanist or histologist that the vessels of a stem or the fibres of a muscle have been knit and soldered by a clever faker than to convince a naturalist, alive to the realities he is handling, of the genetic independence of living groups.[1]

The mass of organic matter that envelops the earth was born and has grown. If it is to retain the certitude we have guaranteed it, this proposition must clearly be kept in the general form we have left it in. Zoological evolution (this follows from the very terms of our proof) is definitely established only to the extent that is necessary to explain the architecture of life. Once we begin to approach the problem more closely, hesitations begin. What exactly are the modalities of birth and growth that governed the establishment of the present equilibrium in the world of life? How many independent biological components are there, that is to say how many primordial phyla? What are the internal or external factors that governed the differentiation and adaptation of forms? What, in a word, are the particular

---

[1] If one reads with some attention the most outspoken attacks made by independent scholars in the last few years against the old forms of transformism, one will immediately see that these apparent adversaries (however pluralist they proclaim themselves) all admit as an indisputable premise, that there is an evolution (that is to say a connected history) of life.

expressions of the physical function that, as we are certain, organic-ally binds beings together? All these questions still remain without definite answers. But at the same time, as we must repeatedly stress, they are secondary to the problem. Even if all the specific content of the Darwinian or Lamarckian explanation of life were to be de-molished (and it is precisely this content that the enemies of transformism are attacking), the fundamental fact of evolution would remain imprinted as deeply as ever on our whole experience of life. It no longer seems possible to defend our vision of the living universe, so far as its phenomena are concerned, without assuming the exist-ence of a perceptible biological development. This is the factual and very firm position that the defenders of evolution must never abandon; they must never let themselves be deflected into secondary discussions of the scientific 'hows' and the metaphysical 'whys'.

Let us take notice. Approached from this direction and in this generalized form (that is to say as a universal and continuous testi-mony of systematics) the evolution of organic matter demands be-lief, independent of all direct perception of any transformation of life at the present time. In common with many observers, I am con-vinced that the modification of zoological forms continues to take place (in exactly the same way as the folds and cracking of the earth's crust) and that only their slowness prevents our seeing them. I am convinced, for example, that everywhere around us races are being formed at the present day, in preparation for the coming of new species. But even if the contrary were to be established, that is to say if the *present* immobility of the biosphere were to be scientifically proved,[1] the necessity of a movement in the past to explain the pre-sent state of things would remain unchanged. Even though the calcareous beds of the Alps are definitely stationary today, it is none

---

[1] It is strange that no one has yet noticed this: the famous objection against zoo-logical evolution, based on the fact that all attempts to obtain stable variations of forms artificially generally fail, proves nothing, because *it proves too much*. It would actually lead to the conclusion that the hundreds of thousands of fixed species recognized by systematics represent so many independent 'creations'. Now no be-liever in a fixed universe dare go as far as this today.

the less certain that they were folded in the past. So one cannot re-strain a smile when one finds certain scientists making their accept-ance of the evolutionary viewpoint depend on the results of an in-quiry into the variability of moss or spinach. These scientists have at least one virtue that they are absorbed and immersed in the fruitful minutiae of their research. But what are we to say of the philosophers who try to construct on a needle-point an edifice to rival one that is gradually rising not only, as we have said, on the general results of a whole science but also, as we shall see, on the vast foundation of our whole sensory knowledge.

B. *Transformism, a Particular Case of Universal History*

We have just briefly but sufficiently swept aside the anti-evolutionist's objection based on the apparent fixity of actual living forms. Another objection, based on 'the absence of intermediate forms' should occupy us longer, because to examine it will lead us to a better under-standing of the close link between the transformist conception of life and the structure, no longer merely of the organic world, but of the world as such.

The discontinuity of the genealogical trees drawn by systematics is beyond dispute; and we have had occasion, several times already in other works, to analyse it in detail. Even our most complete phyla (those of the horse, rhinoceros, elephant and camel, for example) when closely viewed, show themselves not to be formed from a single fibre but composed of little overlapping segments be-longing to a very great number of connecting lines. At the origin of phyla, this phenomenon is more pronounced. We have dwelt at length in the preceding pages on the natural groupings in layers, verticils and lines, that biology, considered as a simple science 'of position', distinguishes in the mass of living creatures. What we omitted to say at this point (in order to simplify our argument) was that these various units only form a whole in the present state of our knowledge if we extend them in imagination one into the other. Better nourished at their extremities, particularly if these extremities themselves stand at the extremity of a branch that has quite recently appeared, zoological branches shed their leaves, then rapidly vanish from our eyes as soon as we try to trace them down to the point where they join a common trunk. The result is that the really known parts of the animal and vegetable world appear to us, as a whole and in detail, as tufts of leaves suspended in the air from certain invisible branches; or rather, to use another comparison, like those conifer fruits whose scales touch, but conceal their basic connections.

The anti-evolutionists attach great importance to this discontinuity of phyla, and generally view it as a death-sentence on transformism. This is their illusion. Not only does the disappearance of the zoological peduncles leave standing an undoubted total structure requiring a scientific explanation which the anti-evolutionists have never attempted to give; but also, properly understood, it provides one of the most reassuring signs that the evolutionary views are right. The lacunary character of phyletic lines, at first sight so disconcerting to transformists, is in reality, if carefully viewed, the most certain indication of a true movement of growth in life.

We ask the zoologists to show the first origin of horses, or of amphibians, or of reptiles. But have we ever thought of asking the archaeologists for the origins of the Semites, the Greeks and the Egyptians? Or of asking the linguists for the origins of Sanskrit, Hebrew or Latin? Or the philosophers for that of the principal streams of thought, morals or religion? Or the jurists, for that of the organizing principles of the family or of property? We have only to put these questions to be perpetually surprised by our ignorance of the beginning of things whose evolutionary nature is doubted by nobody, but whose line of descent is in fact established by no precise document. A famous linguist lately called my attention to the fact that we do not know how the Romance languages connect; strictly speaking, indeed, we cannot prove by any written documents that French derives from Latin. After a period of obscurity, our language appears, one fine day, fully formed in its essentials, just like the first mammals or the first horses. When we reflect on this, the reason for these lacunae, so exactly placed at the most interesting points, appears quite simple. By the erosion of time, the weak parts of the past disappear and things tend automatically to reduce themselves to their broadest and toughest portions. Now in the course of a development of any kind, the phases of shortest duration, of least consistency, of weakest extension are those accompanying the first appearance and early progress: for the crises of birth and growth are short-lived, and generally leave no trace of themselves except their imprint on the future. What are most likely to survive, what, in fact, alone can survive, on the other hand, are the quantitative *maxima* corresponding to exact situations and fixed developments. This is why history in all its fields (ancient history at least, and the more ancient the truer this is) presents us only with a succession of civilizations consisting of established states – of fully created objects, in fact – that succeed one another, like the successive sequences of a cinema film. If some cataclysm were to engulf our present human strata without destroying our steel manufactures, all that palaeontologists would discover on arriving from another planet would be bicycles, cars and aeroplanes of more or less fixed and finished types. The first bicycles, the old 'bone-shakers' of early days, being few and soon replaced, would not be discoverable. It makes us laugh to think of the errors which scientific excavators might commit in imagining that our machines were invented perfect at the start. Is not this exactly the trap into which the anti-evolutionists are continually falling?

We have in fact to remember that, in every realm, owing to a factor mechanically linked to the functioning of time, we tend, as objects to grow more distant, to be able to find them only in their adult form. In asking the zoologist, therefore, as a proof of transformism, to show us the origins of the phylum he has succeeded in constructing, we are wrongly requiring of him something that we do not ask of any explorer of the human strata closer to our own. Moreover, we are asking for something impossible, and betraying our complete ignorance of the age and extent of biological evolution, and of the conditions under which all history works.

In reality all that we can conclude, in zoology, from the absence of intermediate forms, is that since the biosphere, reacts in exactly the same manner to the methods of our historical analysis as everything that we most certainly know to be evolutionary, it is itself evolutionary by nature. By this statement, the objection is transformed into a proof. We had only to generalize it, to discover this very simple truth: that scientific evolution is not simply a hypothesis for the use of zoologists, but a key that anyone can use to enter any room of the past – the key to universal reality. It is either very cunning or very wrong to attribute to biologists alone, as if they alone were responsible for defending it, the grave responsibility for transformist views. The truth is that natural history is merely discovering, on its own territory, the same laws of development and the same lacunae as any other study of the past. To shake transformism in its essence, would be to attack the whole of our science of past reality; would be to upset the whole science of history. Have they ever thought of that, these people who imagine that evolution is ruined because they have found a discontinuity in the girdles of vertebrates that is stronger than it seemed at first? Using transformism as a guide, zoologists in no way pretend (as we shall be forced to repeat) that they are explaining the basis of things. But they do maintain that no animal, any more than Caesar or Sesostris, can appear in the field of our experience except along a line of events and under determinable circumstances. And no one can dispute the correctness of this postulate except, as we shall see, by contradicting the most fundamental and universal laws of our sensory experience.

c *The Discovery of Organic Time or the Basis of Transformism*

Now we have at last arrived, by successive stages, at the root of the transformist question. By attaching transformism to history in general (that is to say in fact to the whole realm of the positive sciences), we have not only made it structurally invulnerable, but have implicitly recognized a fact and put a question of fundamental importance.

Our science of empirical reality today (whether applied to living organisms, ideas, institutions, religions, languages or the constituent elements of matter) tends, in its inquiries and theories, invincibly to adopt the historical method, that is to say the point of view of evolution, of becoming. History is gradually invading all the disciplines from metaphysics to physical chemistry, and we have reached the point where (as I have explained elsewhere) a sort of single science of reality is beginning to take shape: something that we could call 'the natural history of the world'. To what mysterious necessity must we attribute this invasion? What is the reason for this movement?

The answer is this: *We are in process of discovering time.* Time. Always, of course, human experience has been conscious of being immersed in its vast ocean. But there is a great distance between this first over-simple perception of duration, and the deeper comprehension towards which the progressive analysis of the universe is gradually taking us.

Until a quite recent era (till the last century in fact) time remained in practice, for men as a whole, a sort of vast vessel in which things were suspended side by side. In this indifferent and homogeneous field, each being was imagined capable of arising at any moment or place. Lying in this ocean, all natures appeared as clear-cut in their outlines, origin and history as an object suspended in water. It could seemingly be placed, shifted or extracted at will. For Aristotelianism, of course, time was not really different from the movement of things. For this truly profound conception of duration was fundamentally allied with an essential immobilism. A shifting of place, in fact, remained to some extent the *analogum princeps* of movement, and if other changes were envisaged as a means of establishing and dividing duration, these were seemingly nothing more fundamental than sense data, the play of emotions or the idea of intellectual types. The different 'natures' were taken as the ready-made primordial elements of the world. Their possible 'substantial changes' were fixed in advance and instantaneous. In the case of ancient scholasticism, one may wonder if time ever touched anything but the realm of accidents, that is to say the surface aspect of beings.

For the last century, on the other hand, under the impact of the biological sciences and more generally of science as a whole, philosophical thought is turning towards more generalized perspectives. For us duration now permeates the essence of beings to their last fibres.[1] It penetrates into their very stuff; not that things thereby become (as has often been alleged) fluid and inconsistent, but in the sense that today, *however fixed we suppose their nature to be*, they seem to us termless and indefinite during its preparation, maturation and completion. Once considered 'point-like' their 'natures' now stretch indivisibly before our eyes, along the whole length of experiential time. They become to some degree 'threadlike'. At certain moments, no doubt, beings are more precisely 'born'; that is to say they enter definitely into the field of their internal consciousness and of our common experience. But this birth, by which we conventionally make them begin, is preceded in reality by a gestation without assignable origin. By something in itself (is not this what St. Augustine called *ratio seminalis*?) everything is extended into some other preliminary reality, prolonged by something else, everything is found linked in its individual preparation and development (that is to say its own duration) with a general evolution on which cosmic duration records itself. Partially, infinitesimally, without losing any of its individual value, each element is co-extensive with history, with the reality of the whole.

This fundamental condition of beings, that they cannot be perceived except in combination with the whole past, can of course be expressed in metaphysical terms. But what is most important for our argument is that it first of all expresses a law of our perceptual experience. Philosophers like Bergson have merely translated into a

---

[1] One might perhaps put it like this: Aristotelian hylomorphism represents the projection of modern evolution on a world without duration. Transferred to a universe to which duration had added an extra dimension, the theory of matter and form becomes practically indistinguishable from our modern speculations on the development of nature.

general system a condition encountered on all the paths that we try to open into tangible reality. Around us countless things arise, grow and cross the ontological corridors that give them access to higher levels of being. Nothing makes a complete beginning. All things are born from what existed before them. Pascal was astounded by the two abysses of space, the infinitely small and the infinitely great, between which we walk. The most magnificent discovery of our time is undoubtedly that we have become conscious of a third abyss, which gave rise to the other two, the abyss of the past. Since then, for all human thought that is aware of the world, everything has become structurally a sort of bottomless well into which our gaze plunges to lose itself in the infinitude of past time.

We see it today, and no doubt for ever. Just as 'being in space' expresses that primordial law of the world by which *beside* each thing there stands another which sustains and extends it, so 'being in time' signifies, for each reality, that *before* it there stands another to introduce it; and so on, to infinity. An absolute beginning in the very least thing (that is to say the experiential reality of a being, however small, one of whose faces yawned on temporal nothingness) would as surely ruin the entire edifice of our perceptual universe, that is to say would as radically contradict its inner structure, as the existence of a cosmic boundary along which objects would present one face to spatial nothingness. Even organic life on earth, as can easily be foreseen, will appear to us with ever-increasing plainness to be emerging from some 'pre-life'. This is what transformism, in agreement with all the other sciences, says about the realm of living forms; and if it is to be destroyed this certainly must be shaken.

If this be carefully noted, we shall avoid all useless controversy. The perception of organic time of which we are speaking (that is of time whose total unrolling corresponds to the gradual, progressive and irreversible elaboration of a collection of organically linked elements), this new perception, we say, does not offer in itself any explanation of things, but only a more correct view of their quantitative integrity. By the fact that living beings, for example, instead of being confined within a few years of existence, now appear to us as the fruit of a gestation which makes them literally children of the earth and the universe, we come to appreciate more exactly their true dimensions and the immensity of the problem posed by the material existence of the smallest of them.

But it in no way follows that the problems of their external form, and even less of the reason for their existence, are resolved. We find that we have acquired a better idea of their complexity, of their extent and of the uselessness of any physical or philosophical solution that might try to account for elements in isolation from the whole. This is all, neither more nor less. An immense progress in our consciousness of reality and mapping of the world, a more pronounced and justified taste for unitary views and theories; but directly, no new access to the hidden levels of structures and causes. This is what the birth of a historical sense in human thought means to us.

Not only, one might say, does scientific evolution explain nothing, but it recalls and makes palpable to us this elementary truth: however far we extend our experience of the perceptible, we cannot but remain in the perceptible. If we were to meet somewhere, in time or space, an object with no neighbour or an event without antecedent, we should find a fissure through which to look beyond appearances. Now nothing seems capable of piercing the veil of phenomena. When we begin to speak of a universe in which the spatial and temporal series radiate without limit around each element, many minds take fright and we begin to speak of eternal matter. The absence of all empirical beginnings, an essential postulate of transformism and all history, has a more modest and very very different meaning. It in no way entails the existence of a universe invested with divine attributes.[1] All that it means is that the world is so constructed that our perceptions are the absolute prisoners of its immensity. The further our

---

[1] Such a universe has in fact none of the plenitude of being, or the eternal quality that Christian philosophy recognizes in God. Its necessity is a consequence of the free-will of the Creator, and its 'unbounded' character has nothing to do with infinity. From the fact that our mind does not perceive any first link in the chain of phenomena, one cannot conclude the non-existence of an ontological beginning of duration.

mind penetrates, the further its shores seem to recede. Far from tending to discover a new god, science only goes on showing us matter, which is the footstool of the Divinity. One does not draw near to the Absolute by travelling, but by ecstasy. Such is the final intellectual lesson of transformism and its final moral and religious teaching.

D *The Moral Consequences of Transformism*

In appearance discussions on the subject of transformism are on a scientific level. Basically the passion displayed has a deeper origin; it is of a moral and religious order. The opponents of biological evolution would not be so ingenious in multiplying or developing their objections, if they were not inspired by a fundamental distrust of the new ideas; they are persuaded that by attacking the theory of transformism they are defending virtue and religion.

One might be tempted to meet these prejudices by simply ruling them out of court. If in fact transformism is merely applying to the case of animal and plant life a structure common to all material reality, or correlatively a pattern common to our experience, we have seemingly no alternative but to accept it as a law of being, without considering whether we like it or not. But a brusque refusal would be psychologically clumsy and rationally too sweeping. Though often formulated in rather too sentimental a manner, the anti-evolutionists' antipathies have their source in the very proper idea, that a new truth can only be definitely incorporated in human thought if it shows itself capable of nourishing and bringing life to that part of it which already rests on solid foundations. This must be accepted. If the world is explicable (as we all implicitly suppose it is) evolutionary views can only inspire confidence on condition that they do not contradict any of these elements recognized as necessary for the maintenance and conservation of human activity.

Now, as we hear on all sides, evolutionary theory directly threatens this activity. It strikes it at the root by destroying faith in the soul and the Divine. It poisons its workings by placing a doctrine of egoism and brutality above the virtues of goodness and altruism.

A defence of transformism would be gravely defective if it did not take into account these non-scientific objections. We shall therefore refute them by proving that if transformist conceptions have in fact been utilized to serve materialistic and inhuman tendencies this perversion is neither necessary nor legitimate. Correctly understood, transformism is, on the contrary, a possible teacher of spiritual idealism and high morality.

1. *Transformism, a possible school of higher spirituality.* In the first place, transformism does not logically imply either materialism or atheism. What new contribution does it in fact bring to our vision? Nothing less, as we have seen, than an immense chain of 'becoming'. In the world of the senses, it teaches us, the more conscious regularly succeeds the less. Historically and scientifically a 'more' presupposes a 'less'. Thus spirit and matter, commonly regarded as two opposing universes associated for no comprehensible reason, are simply two poles joined by a flux, through which the elements, however ontologically different we suppose them to be, are so governed that they can appear only in one zone; that is to say in a determined order. Strictly speaking, this law of distribution only regulates *appearances*. But as usual our thought cannot refrain from taking one step more than science requires. Where the facts only show a succession of births, it will generally perceive a *link* of being, that is to say will admit that something substantial becomes purer and actually passes from the material to the spiritual pole of the world. Let us take the theory in this extreme form, which can easily be argued in terms acceptable by the most orthodox philosophy. Who will fail to see that this belief favours spiritualism rather than materialism? Would you insist on placing the primacy of being in the plural and unconscious at the risk of making the world unthinkable and incapable of life? Then everything reduced to its lowest terms becomes matter.

Do you not understand, we ask, that on the contrary only union and synthesis make the universe blessed and stable? In order to be, would you not choose to seek the absolute sense of all growth in the direction of this upper pole? In that case, by virtue of the link between things established by evolution, everything is related to the highest; everything becomes, if not spirit, at least distant preparation, spiritized 'matter'.

Do not fear that by accepting this you commit the opposite mistake and fall from materialist pantheism into a spiritual monism, which would exclude the transcendental action of a first cause. What gives many people the impression that in a universe of evolutionary structure the Christian god disappears is that they have not sufficiently reshaped the idea of creation in their minds. They continue to imagine that divine epiphanies will take the form of localized and tangible intrusions, like those accompanying the action of material and secondary causes. Now such violations of our sensible universe by an activity of a higher order, would not only be, to use scholastic language, *contra leges naturae, in essendo et in percipiendo*, (since they would take the form for us of an appearance entering reality without antecedent, which is as we have seen a 'monstrous event'); but they would add nothing to the powers of the creative act.[1]

To be created for the universe is to find oneself in that transcendental relationship to God which makes a man secondary, participated, steeped in the Divine to the very marrow of his being. We have got into the habit (despite our repeated affirmations that creation is not an act in time) of connecting this state of 'participated' being with the existence of an experiential zero in duration, that is to say with a *registrable* temporal beginning. But this alleged requirement of orthodoxy can only be substantiated by an illegitimate contamination of the phenomenal plan by the metaphysical. Let us reflect for a moment and we shall see that in order to exercise itself in the world, the property of divine action is precisely not to be observed either here or there (except to some degree in the mystical relationship of spirit with Spirit) but to be spread throughout the sustained, completed and to some extent super-animated complex of secondary activities. Whether our space and time have an ascertainable limit or not in no

---

[1] Of course an actual miracle is not a violation of phenomena so much as a harmonious extension (by *super-creation* or *super-animation*) of the powers of the created being.

way affects the operation of a higher force, the property of which is precisely that it is applied to the global totality of the world, past, present and future.

In no way irreconcilable with the idea of a creation when it suggests an unbounded sensible universe,[1] transformism is not materialistic or atheistic either when it offers the image of a world in which human thought appears at its due moment in organo-physical connection with the lower forms of life. Many people think that the superiority of the spirit would not be safe unless its first manifestation were accompanied by some interruption of the ordinary course of the world. Just because it is spirit, one should say in refutation, its appearance must have taken the form of a crowning or blossoming. But let us put aside all systematic considerations. Is it not true that every day innumerable human souls are 'created' in the course of an embryogenesis so continuous that no scientific observation will ever find the smallest break in the chain of biological phenomena? There we have daily before our eyes the example of a creation, absolutely imperceptible and undetectable by pure science. Why should we make difficulties in the case of the first man? Admittedly, it is *much* more difficult to imagine the appearance of 'reflexion' along a phylum formed of different individuals than along a series of states traversed by the same embryo. But, from the point of view of the creative act considered in its relations with phenomena, the case of ontogenesis is the same as that of phylogenesis. Why not admit, for example, that the absolutely free and special action by which the Creator decided that humanity should crown His work so influenced and pre-organized the course of the world before man, that he now appears to us (as a result of the Creator's choice) to be the fruit naturally expected by the developments of life? *Omnia propter hominem.* If this intention be translated into preliminary operations, we have the exact picture of an evolution which implies from its beginnings the appearance of thought on earth. Let us be careful, once more, not to

[1] Since, let us repeat, it does not at all follow from the fact that the temporal beginning of the world is, from the phenomenal point of view, not to be found that the notion of an ontological beginning of the universe has no reality.

confuse levels. In our universe discontinuities of nature, the evolutionary stages (as numerous and important as philosophy requires) imply no necessary pause in the development of phenomena.[1]

If there is a difference between the transformist and 'fixist' manners of understanding the human soul, it is that for the former the soul has not only been specially, but *uniquely* willed. The Creator has not merely thrown it one fine day into a world artificially prepared to receive it. He has caused it to be born for the first time, and He continues to cause it to be born each day, by an action marvellously geared from the beginning to the progress of the universe. This view is certainly better suited than any other to give our modern minds a high speculative idea of the value of the spirit. But it has another superiority, which it remains for us to analyse : that of introducing into the very course of our practical life a high degree of idealism and reponsibility.

2. *Transformism, a possible school of high morality.* There is no sophism more damaging to ideological discussion than to apply to the whole of a theory the weaknesses that it presents in one or another of its particular aspects. By identifying transformism with its mechanistic or materialist forms and more especially with Darwinism, many have misjudged it. In these last years (as a somewhat strange after-effect of the war) there has been a recrudescence of the crusade against the corrupting effects of evolution, understood as a synonym of the struggle for life. Transformism (it has been said, and not only in Tennessee) is a school of immorality, because in the name of natural selection it first justifies and then teaches a selfish struggle, the precedence of force over right. We will not even try to discover, in this study, whether the ideas of that great scientist Darwin are correctly expressed in the simplified argument that I have just quoted. But, taking this vulgar and widespread interpretation of the moral

[1] So, philosophically speaking, the extension to man of transformism (taken in the general sense, the only one admitted here, of historical linkage between the general developments of life) – this extension, I say, demanded by the whole of our biological knowledge, can present no serious difficulties to a Christian thinker.

consequences of transformism as our point of departure and basis of discussion, we should like to point out that we have only to set the sails of our ship differently and more correctly, and the wind of evolution, reputed so destructive, will sweep us magnificently towards the highest idealism.

We must always start from the same solid base: the essential of transformism is not to introduce some particular mechanism into our explanation of life's developments. Transformism is the vision simply of an organic universe, and more especially an organic world, whose parts are physically linked together both in their appearance and their destiny.

In this view, what do we think should be the one legitimate effect of the evolutionary viewpoint of a man deeply convinced of its truth?

Such a man would see in the first place the greatness of his responsibilities increasing almost to infinity before him. Hitherto he could think of himself in nature as a bird of passage, local, accidental, free to waste the spark of life that is given him, with no loss to anyone but himself. Suddenly he finds in his heart the fearful task of conserving, increasing and transmitting the fortunes of a whole world. His life, in a true sense, has ceased to be private to him. Body and soul, he is the product of a huge creative work with which the totality of things has collaborated from the beginning; if he refuses the task assigned to him, some part of that effort will be lost for ever and lacking throughout the whole future. What awe must the atom feel when it finds the face of the universe reflected in its heart! What a miraculous sound, could we but hear them, would be the groans that attended our birth mingled with appeals coming to us from the future! For the briefest moment the success of the whole affair, of this huge universal childbirth, actually rests in the hands of the least among us. These are the holy words which everyone must try to say, but which the evolutionist, most of all, has the true right to repeat. Because, in his theories, all juridical or nominal relationships between the elements of the world have given way to organic and natural connections, the cost and importance of life have acquired a new value for him. His eyes have become more perceptive of the greatness of the universe; and at the same time his heart has effortlessly opened to the breadth of Christian love.

The fundamental obstacle to Christian love is in effect numbers. Recently it was written in a book that has given rise to a social movement: 'It is impossible sincerely to love everyone'. The heart of each of us is full when it is given to one other. Therefore, if we set out to love the human mass, we are false to ourselves; or rather we deceive ourselves. We are making an effort against nature. The clear truth is that simple justice, with its cool economy, must replace this impossible sentiment in human relations.

If humanity merely formed a collection of units in physical juxtaposition, or merely divergent, it would be difficult to confute this new Gospel. The Christian injunction to love your neighbour essentially presumes that men are not only brothers by common descent (which would still be insufficient in itself rightfully to subdue egoism and command love), but can in a real and physical manner recognize one another as members of a single passionately desired being. However, not everyone is capable of immediately accepting supernatural views of the Incarnation, and moreover, these views, to be truly living, demand, even in the strongest believers,[1] reliance on the pre-existent perception of a natural human unity: the preparation and foundation of a higher unity *in Christo Jesu*.

From what direction will the first ray of light strike the intellect, and reveal to it, beneath the repulsive dust of humanity the outline of a single and unique reality, which it is possible to love? From the direction of evolution.

Seen from a standpoint that is both evolutionary and spiritual,[2] the

---

[1] Always in virtue of the great 'law of birth', which governs both the movements of psychological life and the transformation of the organic world.

[2] By spiritual evolutionism we understand that theory (defined on p. 133–4) which places the true future of the world's development and being on the side of the spirit, that is to say of synthesis. This evolutionary theory, which depends on a belief in a higher pole of the universe might be called an evolutionism by convergence. Evolutionisms of 'divergence', whether radically materialist (that is to say placing

world is not only charged, as I have said, with a formidable responsibility, but infused from the humblest level of belief in God, with an irresistible attraction. Then we know indeed, that a small number of privileged creatures is incapable of satisfying the essential need of love and completion in each man. But thanks to these rare creatures, and as a reflection of them, the totality of beings engaged with him in the unifying work of the cosmos will do so. No unit can finally find happiness except by reunion with the whole and the transcendent centre required to move that whole. Consequently, if it is psychologically impossible for him to surround each being with the distinct and overflowing affection characteristic of human love, he can at least cultivate towards all things that general warmth (inchoate but genuine) which will make him cherish in each object (over and above all sensible qualities) its very being. Being, that is to say that indefinable and chosen portion of each thing which becomes little by little, through God's influence, the flesh of his flesh.

Love of this kind is not exactly comparable with any attachment known in ordinary social relations. Its 'material object', as the schoolmen would say, is so vast, and its 'formal object' so profound that it can only be translated into complex terms of espousals and adoration. In it all distinction between egoism and altruism tends to disappear. Each man loves and seeks himself in the consummation of all the rest: and the smallest urge to possession extends into an effort to attain, in the most distant future, that which is the same in all.

Reflecting on these various effects of evolutionary views (properly understood) on our conduct, we come to wonder whether their

---

the equilibrium of the world in multiplicity) or simply renouncing all hope in an ulterior unification of spiritual monads (regarded as a scattering of glowing sparks) are incapable of implanting a sense of universal responsibility and love. They may make all men and everything else in the world into brothers as firmly united in the womb of Demeter as in that of any Eve. But brothers can be enemies; and if they are not, it is for reasons other than their common origin. Birth, after all, is only a memory. The existence of love depends on a common growth in the womb of a single future.

appearance and diffusion, far from being as diabolical as some allege, have not rather, in our age, a providential character.

In so far as it is possible to understand the psychological tendencies of our time, one has the impression that (despite or because of a tremendous drive towards human unity) we are passing through a critical phase of individualism. Certainly, never at any moment in history has a sharper sense of the rights of each unit been more general in all social groups. Rights of man, rights of the citizen, rights of the worker, rights of peoples, to act, to think, to develop freely have been exalted both in the personal and the collective mind. We hate even the idea of an unjustified external interference with our (autonomous) powers of judgement and action. It would be useless to regret and condemn this awakening, which undoubtedly represents an advance in the state of the thinking units in the universe. But in the course of all progress, each step, whether to left or right, has to be corrected by the next step. In present day humanity, excess of individualism threatens to bring to matter a fragmentation, dispersion, and consequent return to multiplicity. Everyone tends to neglect the common good. The most natural groupings fall apart. Certitudes slowly gained by the experience and reflexion of ages disappear. A kind of rebellious independence becomes the ideal moral attitude. Intellectually, this dispersion of past efforts and thoughts takes the form of agnosticism.

What do the men of our century need to compensate the ills that an insufficiently balanced perception of individual values will bring? How can this evil be turned to the benefit of further progress? They must at all costs rediscover, at the level of their present thought, the sense of totality. It must become their dominant passion.

When each man, by virtue of a conception of the world that demands only a minimum of metaphysics, and that is supported, moreover, by the greatest number of arguments from experience, will admit that his true being is not limited to the narrow boundaries of his limbs and his historical existence but that he forms part, body and soul, of the process that drives the universe, then he will understand that, in order to remain faithful to himself he must devote himself to the task demanded of him by life as to a personal and sacred duty. Then he will regain belief in the world, in a world whose totality cannot perish, and also faith in a supreme centre of personalization, concentration and cohesion, the only point at which the salvation of the universe can be conceived to take place.

And this will be, more than ever, the world ripe for conversion: *anima naturaliter christiana.*

Thus evolutionism, far from being a peripheral or perverse doctrine, is bound up with the broadest and deepest movements of human growth. As we have already observed, in the intellectual realm it expresses the incursion into all our scientific views of a better understanding of the nature of organic time.

We now perceive that in the moral and religious sector, it accompanies and supports the rise of universalist views and aspirations which are even more characteristic of our modern age then any surge of individualism. The enemies of transformism still consider it a little stone that they can kick away. Let them try to dig round this stone and they will discover that it is part of the bone fabric of the new earth.

This is what we have been trying to prove throughout the last pages. Starting from very humble zoological considerations, we have found ourselves insensibly led to analyse the most fundamental conditions of human knowledge and activity. We hope to have shown that the real transformist question is not just a simple dispute over detail that can be decided in the course of an osteological discussion. Relieved of all false or peripheral problems, into which discussion generally strays, it reduces itself to the following dilemma, which must be faced sooner or later.

Either you must admit that nothing can enter the realm of experience without being introduced by some precursor, in which case you are entirely an evolutionist. Or else you believe that a thing can appear without being 'born', and then you are starting an impossible battle with the very structure of the *perceptual* world.

Transposed now into the realm of action, the same dilemma takes another less evident but perhaps more decisive form:

Either you regard the world as a collection of physically linked beings, travelling by way of growth as a whole towards an organic consummation; and then, once more you are in your heart an evolutionist. Or else you see in the universe nothing but a system of moral and juridical relationships by which contiguous beings are associated; and then you have lost all rightful means of restraining the advance of egoistic and agnostic individualism which threatens to dissolve and sweep away the thinking zone of the earth.

Unpublished, Bay of Bengal – Ascension Day, 1926.
The last pages are loosely written and were perhaps left unrevised. [Transl. note].

CHAPTER IX

THE MOVEMENTS OF LIFE

One of the most important advances made by the human mind during last century was the scientific conquest of the illusion of immobility in the realm of the very great and the very small. Beneath the apparent impassivity of matter, we now see a violent movement of atoms and a slow transformation of the physico-chemical elements. In the earth's fixed countenance we can read the unfinished revolutions of a long history. Now the world of living creatures in its turn begins to quake, and reveals itself with growing distinctness to be activated by broad general currents.

In actual fact, it is more than a century since the eyes of natural scientists began to open to the mobility of life. A century ago Lamarck, followed by Darwin (to cite only two representative names in a whole movement of thought), noticed that the branches, classes, families, kinds and species of the Linnaean classifications formed, in their distribution, no fixed system but the outline of an evolution in nature.

But, phenomenal though this first discovery of mobility beneath immobility was in its nascent freshness, it was still, as we now see, much constricted and over simplified. In the eyes of the nineteenth century transformists, living forms actually few in number, must have succeeded one another, end to end, along the line of geological time, following scattered lines along which a uniform movement flowed. The horse immediately after the *Hipparion* and the *Palaeotherium*, man directly following the anthropoids, the mammals exactly continuing the line of the reptiles, amphibians and fish, all this without breaks, each stage passing into the next in all its features. This is hardly an exaggeration of the idea of zoological evolution in its earliest form.

The object of this article is briefly to show how our ideas of the terrestrial developments of organized matter have gradually increased in scope and complexity since the time of the first transformists.

Let us now try to explain what novelties the most recent researches permit us to see or glimpse in the variety and breadth of life's movements.

A *The Variety of Life's Movements*

The simplest and first perceived of life's movements is that which along a chain or line of living beings (along a phylum, as one says) produces the gradual accentuation of a particular type of organism: horse-type, elephant-type, cat-type, etc.

The known number of such phyla is constantly increasing (horses, camels, elephants, rhinoceros, deer, etc.) and one may say that there is today no single type of mammal whose formation we cannot trace over a considerable space of time. It might seem therefore that we are now coming very close to the solution of the problem of living species. Not yet. And for this reason:

The phyla correspond, as we were saying, each one to a particular mode of organization. They mark the stages followed by life in constructing certain living tools, like the single-toed hoof of a horse, the carnivore's teeth, the adaptation to swimming of a seal, etc. But what do they teach us about the actual origin of the movement which thus guided living beings in this or that morphological direction? Nothing. Even supposing that we push it very far, our success in reconstructing genealogical lines could not bring us a satisfactory solution of the problem of living forms. The movements of linear evolution, to which scientists have for so long been trying to reduce transformism, are like those fine straight shoots that one sees springing from the trunk of a tree. Follow them down. They end at a fork, that is to say what once was a bud. Life too must bud and divide; otherwise the very existence of phyla would be inconceivable. So we come to an unavoidable conclusion. When we consider the phenomena of continuous birth in one direction (orthogenesis), we are compelled to pay increasing attention and give a larger and larger place to movements of an absolutely different nature: to sudden changes of form or, as they are called, mutations.

Mutations or, as we have just explained, the births of new biological orientations are beginning to be clearly noted by zoologists and botanists. Nevertheless, because they are by nature rapid, and only lead to a beginning or embryo of morphological change, and only affect a limited number of individuals, to observe them directly is extremely difficult in the case of living forms, and practically impossible in that of fossils. But, fortunately, though we can hardly see the mutations themselves we can detect certain general laws which they obey, and which consequently allow us to see them by a sort of secondary impression.

In this respect, one could say that in a given group of living creatures the mutations can act (and thereby show themselves) in at least three ways: by dispersion, by radiations, by canalization.

By *dispersion*, first: when the creatures under consideration differentiate in every direction within their type, like a beam of white light refracted in a continuum of vibrations on one plane. The countless forms, at the same time so fixed and so closely related, that we find in certain kinds or families of butterflies, fish, birds, antelopes – true variations on a single zoological theme – visibly reveal a fragmentation of this kind.

By *radiations*, next: when the new variations, instead of scattering without greatly separating, follow a limited but progressive number of directions, clearly determined by precise conditions of existence and surroundings. In the case of vertebrates, natural scientists long ago discovered the law of diversification and balance that compels any isolated fauna (provided it is sufficiently important) to divide itself into a number of phyla: that is to say into runners, climbers, swimmers, burrowers, long-distance flyers, herbivores, carnivores, insectivores, etc. Examples of this are the reptiles in the Secondary, mammals in the Tertiary; the marsupials isolated in Australia, or the placentals once upon a time confined to South America.

By *canalization*, lastly: when the very strongly 'polarized' changes of form converge, and move all together in a common direction. Which allows us a new glimpse of the phyla themselves, at a deeper level. We can (as we have up to now) simply consider each phylum as a continuous line of development. But this is merely a scheme with no explanation. By pushing our analysis further, we perceive that any zoological line, that of horses for example, is probably nothing but a directed series of small and numerous mutations.

Of course in each of these three cases (dispersion, radiations, canalization), and in the first two especially, the actions of mutation are not continuous but periodic. The secondary shoots of a plant neither detach themselves nor grow uniformly on the trunk that bears them. There is a rhythm in the ramification and growth of plants. Likewise in the differentiation of living forms. For a long time a zoological branch appears fixed. Then it begins to grow again or becomes the centre of a bundle of new branches, which in their turn either proliferate or become fixed. Is not this exactly what is happening all around us in human society, to individuals, families, races, nations?

As a result of the repeated movements of budding and bifurcation that we have just analysed, the genealogical tree of past and present living forms is in reality an inconceivably complex bush. Palaeontologists are becoming increasingly aware today that even in the most promising cases we never succeed in following a true genealogical line for long, in tracing our phyla along a continuous line. Our straightest series are actually made up of a host of little overlapping segments, corresponding each to a separate form; and these forms replace one another like tangents along the line of a curve. The types of horse, rhinoceros, man that we arrange in a sequence of descent are no more than very distant cousins; they replace rather than follow one another.

We meet here the great law of 'relaying', which governs all that we can see of the past. It is an imperious law which, to be fully understood, requires that when we have paused to observe the variety of life's moments we shall then try to take some account of their extent.

B *Extent of Life's Movements*

Like the material sciences, though from a different viewpoint, the sciences of life are gradually led, by their very progress, to become a study of large numbers. Today, one would understand nothing about zoological evolution if one did not previously absorb the idea (in a visionary way, if possible), that it is a play of masses, the effect of masses.

Let us first think of the thousands of millions of individuals who are at present divided into thousands of species, each in their turn stemming from the ten branches into which systematics has divided the animals alone. There is not one of these individuals that does not to some degree represent a possible centre of mutation. Here, measured in an instantaneous section, is the quality and complexity of life, which for millions of years has unceasingly swerved this way and that in a thousand various streams within this organic envelope of the earth that is called the biosphere. It is a far cry from these innumerable and cross-connecting threads to the few simple bifurcating lines to which the natural scientist reduces his genealogical constructions when he draws them on a sheet of paper.

Assuredly, translated into the realm of actual life in which the connections are so numerous that it would require a space of n dimensions to draw it in satisfactory outline, the various elementary movements of transformation here analysed (orthogenesis, mutations . . .) still remain essentially valid. But they are contained in other kinds of movements, proper to very great unities; it is here that they find their necessary complement, here that they begin to become clear. What often makes certain vital phenomena difficult to explain is that we try to imagine or reproduce them in far too small a field. If we enlarge our horizons, we shall be right in thinking that we are beginning to see more clearly.

Once life has taken on the characteristics and properties of a vast crowd, it reveals itself as capable of the many momentary gropings and perpetual pressure in all directions that our theories require. We then see that in the process of vegetable or animal transformations, it has tried almost all morphological solutions and found all the answers during its long history.

Once it no longer forms a little discontinuous group in our eyes, but a vast reservoir of connected elements, life itself becomes the possible seat of these processes of gestation and maturation without which certain major mutations (the one for example which must have produced humanity) remain unintelligible. Obscurely, the new orientations can prepare and incubate in the ferment of the living mass, till the day when they burst out from all directions and multiply. In the same way all the branches simultaneously grow green in the forest in the first fine weather. In the same way, one fine morning a revolution breaks out in the realm of humanity and renews the face of ideas and things.

Once its size and appearance have become wavelike, even oceanic, this same life seems always quite naturally to be swept by those periodic tides of which palaeontology and bio-geography show us such graphic traces. Just now we pointed for the first time to that natural law of 'relaying' by which all perceptible changes in life, instead of taking place in a continuous manner, operate in a series of successive waves which replace and pass beyond one another. Reptiles replacing amphibians, mammals succeeding reptiles, man eliminating all the mammals other than himself, all this on the largest scale; species supplanting species, race driving out race, individuals taking the place of individuals, all this on the smallest. The mechanical reason for this particular rhythm of birth must most probably be sought in number: the vast number of living beings. It is because of the effect of masses that in our researches into the past we never seize the actual beginnings, but only the traces of successive waves towering before they break, a series of crests scudding across the seas of the biosphere.

For the first transformists these waves seemed to come from fairly near, or even from quite near. Did they not expect to find plants different from ours in the tombs of ancient Egypt? Now we know that the pulsations which produced the forms all around us lie so far back that the various morphological lines emanating from them seem almost parallel for as far as we can follow them. Another effect and proof of the immensity of the movements running through life.

And now let us take a step further, the one before the last possible in the present state of our knowledge. We have spoken of fumblings, of maturation, of oscillations. But for these effects, these movements to take place, and to do so usefully surely presupposes that the world of living beings, more even than that of atoms and fluids, constitutes a whole, subject to laws of correlation and cohesion. It clearly does so. Just as science required 'isostasis', for example, which geologists use to explain the equilibrium of continents on a relatively liquid zone of the earth, we now seem imperiously in need of a certain 'isotony' to regulate and harmonize the general displacements of the living mass in movement.

Physically, life is one on account of some factor of its own. But now natural scientists have been brought by stages to ask themselves the final question: 'Deeper and vaster than the detailed movements, the minute analysis of which has been till now the principal occupation of transformist biology, must there not be a fundamental movement, capable of scientific definition, of the totality of life?'

It seems that from this point we can begin to answer Yes to the supreme question. First of all, and without abandoning the realm or methods of the material sciences, we are already in a position to observe that life, on the global scale, manifests itself as a current opposed to entropy. Entropy, as is known, is the name that physics gives to that apparently inevitable fall by which collections of corpuscles (the scene of all physico-chemical phenomena) slide, by virtue of statistical laws of probability, towards an intermediate state of diffuse agitation, a state in which all exchange of useful energy ceases on our scale of experience. Everything around us seems to be descending towards this death of matter; everything except life. Opposing the levelling play of entropy, is life, a methodical construction, ceaselessly enlarged, of a building that grows continually more improbable. Protozoa, metazoa, societies of beings, man, humanity, each a mounting defiance against entropy; each an increasingly vast exception to the habitual play of energetics and chance.

Doubtless it has hitherto been possible for physics to keep life within the general laws of thermodynamics. Life, we can still say, is a local counter-current, an eddy in entropy. It is the weight that rises by virtue of a heavier weight that descends. Despite the hindrance caused by this local anomaly, the entire system of nature continues to decline towards universal exhaustion.

If our only evidence of life's movements came from external energetic factors, we could more easily accept its explanation in terms of entropy alone. But there is another aspect of things to be considered. Life taken as a whole does not manifest itself to our experience only as an advance into improbability. It also appears in the light of our scientific investigation as a continuous ascent towards greater consciousness. Beneath the ups and downs of the countless waves of organic forms runs a constantly mounting tide towards greater freedom, inventiveness and thought. Can we possibly think of this tremendous event as merely a secondary effect of cosmic forces? Can we view it as only a subordinate feature of the universe? For metaphysics, there is hardly a possible hesitation. For physics the question is just being put.

It will, we hope, be a future task for science to draw a general picture of things which will synthesize the two apparently opposed phases of entropy and life. Let us merely note here that it has been the achievement of our century to discover once and for all that these are the two great currents identifiable by experience which between them divide the world.

Unpublished, April 1928.

CHAPTER X

WHAT SHOULD WE THINK OF
TRANSFORMISM?

The question of transformism continues to be passionately discussed; and the introduction of its theories (more or less simplified or perverted) in schoolbooks obliges Christian schoolmasters to have precise ideas on what is certain or doubtful, acceptable or unacceptable to believers in the new views. For it is as dangerous to deny too much as to concede too much.

Having lived for many years among the discussions that transformism raises and the realities that it studies, we think it would be useful to mark out as clearly as possible some fundamental principles that will allow anyone to get a fair idea of the transformist question in its present phase.

PRINCIPLE I – Not to confuse a fundamental viewpoint (established) with secondary explanations (frail) in Transformism

We have heard a great deal in the last few years about transformism being in decline. This fall from favour actually affects only certain particular forms of transformism, in which the essential evolutionary idea is associated either with particular explanations or certain philosophical views, such as Darwinism (natural selection), Lamarckism (adaptation under the influence of surroundings), and more generally all the naïve theories that try to reduce the development of life to a few lines of simple evolution followed by a uniform movement under the influence of purely mechanical factors (transformisms of the Haeckel type). True enough, none of these different individual theories is any longer considered satisfactory, for life appears to us more and more complicated every day.

But, even so, there remains the essential transformist view (that is to say that living forms constitute a natural association of things, connected in such a way that we can picture to ourselves scientifically the history of their successive appearances and expansions). There remains this general view, I repeat, which is increasingly accepted (at least implicitly) by all natural scientists. There is not one of the millions of facts daily noted by specialists in classification, comparative anatomy or physiology that is not in full agreement with it. *Everything is classifiable*, that is to say everything finds its natural place (spatial and temporal) each day in the general history of the earth. This is an enormous fact: the veritable proof that the sensible appearance and progressive stages of life obey an empirical law, that is to say can be treated by science as a phenomenon.

It must be carefully observed therefore that, underlying the particular transformist theories (useful but unstable), there exists a transformist 'conception' of the world, and that this probably marks a definite orientation of human thought. Properly understood, this orientation is quite simple and well-based: *transformism is, at bottom, no more than an admission that we can plot the history of life* as we plot the history of human civilizations or of matter. All empirical reality is, by nature, historical (capable of narration). How by what unthinkable miracle, could life escape from this universal condition?

Thus understood, transformism is no longer a simple hypothesis. It is a general method of research, accepted in practice by all scholars. More broadly still, it is merely the extension to zoology and botany of a form of science (historical science) which is continually extending its rule over all human sciences (physics and chemistry, the study of religions, institutions, etc). N.B. It is not our aim to criticize here the anti-transformist ('fixist') position. For clarity's sake, however, it is as well to make these observations:

1. The surprising and indefinite connections by which living species are grouped both in order of succession and, so to speak, organically, confront us with a *positive* scientific problem (as positive as the relative movement of the earth and the sun), which consequently demands a *positive* solution *of a scientific order*. The 'fixists''

great weakness is that they criticize the transformist solution in an entirely negative way, that is to say without proposing any constructive scientific explanation of a fact which they are just as bound to explain as the transformists.

2. The 'fixists'' three great objections to transformism are: (*a*) the impossibility of artificially varying even the smallest species distinguished by systematics, (*b*) the palaeontologists' inability to discover the exact origin of the numerous evolutionary branches, (*c*) the persistence without change of certain living forms throughout geological time. Faced with the enormous fact of the 'natural' (geographical, morphological, and temporal) distribution of living forms, these objections, in my opinion, vanish into non-existence. Let me add also, as a general observation, that they are valueless because *they prove too much*. The first objection would compel the acceptance of a separate 'creation' for hundreds of thousands of species of plants, insects, fish and birds, so closely related and so finely distinguished that no fixist, to my knowledge, dares to attribute a separate origin to them. The two other objections, pushed to the extreme, would cause us to doubt whether the Whites, the Yellowskins and the Blacks, the Egyptians, the Greeks and the Romans, etc., had a common origin since we do not know the starting-point of any human population (or language, or institution, or religion) and that these human departments bristle with examples of survival as characteristic as those of the *Ligulae* or the ginkgo! The fixists' 'great objections' simply point to characteristics or weaknesses that are to be found in any historical science.

PRINCIPLE II – *Not to confuse the scientific plane (of empirical succession in time) with the philosophical plane (of an underlying causality)*

This second principle reminds us of a banal distinction to which we must constantly return.

Scientifically, as we have just stated, transformism merely sets out to recount a history, that is to say to plot a combination of facts and links of a photographic kind (a film): before the living form N, it says, there was the form N-1, which was preceded by the form N-2, and so on. Everything, in our experience is empirically introduced by something else: it 'is born'. This is what transformism affirms.

Now, by virtue of what inner power and with a view to what 'ontological' growth, does this birth take place? Pure science does not know, and it is philosophy's task to decide.

It is a curious fact that this very simple distinction between antecedents (or visible succession) and underlying causality has for long been unperceived. On the appearance of transformism everyone, believers and unbelievers alike, actually imagined that 'to put living forms into temporal connection' was to 'identify them ontologically'; as if, in the course of the evolutionary series, once they were scientifically established, the greater could, *ipso facto*, be considered as springing of its own accord from the less (or, to be more exact, as remaining the less). Nothing could be more wrong or more dangerous than this confusion between 'succeeding' and 'being the same thing'. To connect is not to render identical. Is not each one of us more than the cell from which he sprang? Does the photographic continuity of the states traversed in the course of embryogenesis argue against the appearance of a soul on the way?

This must be thoroughly understood, once and for all, and it must be taught to others. Even when we accept the transformist theory, the place remains open – indeed it yawns more widely than ever – for a primal creative power. And even better, a creation of evolutionary type (God *making things make themselves*) has for long seemed to some very great minds the most beautiful form imaginable in which God could act in the universe. Was it not St. Thomas who, comparing the viewpoint (fixist as we should call it today) of the Latin Fathers like St. Gregory, to the evolutionary viewpoint of the Greek Fathers and St. Augustine, said of the latter, '*Magis placet*' – it is more pleasing (II Sent, d. 12; Q.I.a.2) – Let us be glad to strengthen our minds by contact with this great thought![1]

[1] On the evolutionary thought of the Greek Fathers, see Canon de Dordolot's remarkable little book *Darwinisme et Catholicisme*, Brussels, Vromont, 1914.

PRINCIPLE III – *Correctly to pinpoint the present difficulty in conciliating the scientific and Catholic pictures of human origins*

Science is at present feeling hesitantly for the best way of attaching man historically to the other animals. While the majority of natural scientists continue to suppose that the hominians detached themselves towards the end of the Tertiary age from the group of other anthropoids, some anthropologists and palaeontologists (notably Professor Osborn) now tend to imagine a far earlier separation for our group and a far longer autonomy. In their opinion man represents, on the primate trunk, a zoological branch parallel to that of the anthropoids but differing from it.

These discussions may have given the uninitiated the impression that the theory of human descent is losing ground. Actually, the controversy (like that on the heredity of acquired characteristics) only touches on secondary characteristics of transformism. Fundamentally, and more than ever in the eye of the immense majority of natural scientists, man is coming back (and increasingly so) into the general transformist perspective. The more one examines our zoological type, scientifically, the more irresistibly one is led to admit that neither the coincidence of its appearance with that of the other great anthropoids, nor the minute details of its anatomical agreement with them,[1] nor the characteristics of the fossil remains (still rare but significant[2]) we possess, can reasonably be explained without some

---

[1] It is almost impossible, for example, to distinguish a human molar from a chimpanzee's. Now a mammal's tooth is something perfectly definite; an organ rich in homologues with a whole history of its own.

[2] Since these lines are written in China, let me say that last year, some kilometres from Peking, in the course of extensive excavations, scientifically conducted in a fossil-bearing fissure containing remains of animals of the Quaternary age, some remains (fragments of jaws and skulls) were discovered belonging to a being of a very strange zoological type. The teeth are certainly, and the skull probably of human type, but the shape of the mandible recalls the chimpanzee. Before forming a definite judgement on these documents we must obviously wait until they have been completely separated from their accretions, which are extremely hard. But we seem to be confronted with a serious fact that deserves to hold everyone's attention.

historical (that is to say empirically disappointing) link between him and the other primates.

Here more than anywhere is the place to remember that to put two beings even into genealogical connection is not necessarily to 'make them one'. Often the religious revolt *a priori* against the views of our past presented by transformism. They are wrong. Philosophically the Christian, as such, would have no good reason to deny, *in principle*, an extension of scientific evolution to man or to be afraid if this extension became one day imperative. Why could not the formation of the human *species*, like that of every human *individual* have been evolutionary? Was it not St. Thomas, once again, who said somewhere, that he would be even more pleased if God had drawn man '*ex limo jam informato*'?[1]

If there is anything in modern scientific views that still very greatly disturbs Catholic thought, it is not the possible derivation of man (a spiritual being) from the animals. It is the difficulty of making a plausible reconciliation between transformism (once accepted) and a *strict monogenism*, that is to say our common descent from a single couple. On the one hand, for reasons which are not definitely philosophical or exegetic but essentially *theological* (the Pauline conception of the Fall and Redemption), the church clings to the historical reality of Adam and Eve. On the other, for reasons of probability and also comparative anatomy, science, left to itself, would never (to say the least of it) dream of attributing so narrow a basis as two individuals to the enormous edifice of humankind.

This is the precise point around which the provisional disagree-

---

[1] From still unformed clay. We must of course be careful not to let ourselves be guided in these matters by questions of feeling or sensitiveness. As if it were more repugnant to feel oneself joined to an animal stock than to the earth itself! Nothing in nature is low and inferior once one considers it *in motion* towards being and the light of God.

Readers who want a sound and moderate explanation of the present state of our knowledge of prehistory will do well to read one of the following books: M. Boule, *Les Hommes fossiles* (latest edition) or G. Goury, *Origine et Evolution de l'Homme*, Paris, Picard.

ment between science and faith on the subject of transformism today revolves. It is, in my opinion, a definite step towards the solution of the conflict that the problem should be clearly defined.

What will the solution be? It is impossible to say yet. The two fragments of truth confronting us will never be joined together before being made perfectly clear. Now on the subject of human origins science has certainly much more to discover, and Catholics much more thinking to do. All that can be foreseen is that the Church will increasingly recognize the scientific validity of an evolutionary form of creation; and science will in the end give a larger place to the powers of the mind, of liberty, and therefore of 'improbability', in the historical evolution of the world. Monogenism will then without losing any of its theological 'efficiency', gradually assume a form fully conforming to our scientific requirements.

In the meantime the proper attitude for the believer cannot be in doubt. He has merely to seek, patiently and confidently, *on both sides*. Faith guarantees that there can be no contradiction between his creed and human knowledge.

PRINCIPLE IV – *Utilizing the views of scientific transformism, to construct a spiritual theory of evolution more probable and more seductive than materialist evolution.*

In the preceding observations we have maintained a largely defensive position towards the teachings of evolution. 'To what extent does transformism compel scientific acceptance? To what limits is it philosophically and theologically probable? It is now necessary to take the offensive, not in order to destroy but to conquer. Transformism is generally regarded as antichristian by nature. Would it not be more just (and apologetically more efficacious) to claim that it is capable of forming an excellent basis for Christian thought and action?

This seems to be so.

Let us imagine for a moment that we basically adopt the historical explanation of the world given by transformism. What effect would it have on our intellectual judgement and practical conduct of life? None other, if I judge correctly, than *to enhance our estimation of spiritual values*, both in the field of intellectual viewpoint and moral actions.

1. *First in the intellectual field*. It must be confessed that at first glance, by its manner of reducing living beings to ever more elementary organisms and ever more simplified mechanisms, transformism may give the impression that it is 'materializing' the universe. But this impression derives from the fact that we are following it in its work of analysis, that is to say, in a manner of speaking, *downwards*. Starting from the lowest terms at which it arrives, let us try, *moving upwards*, to appreciate the work of synthesis implied in the fitting together of the pieces that our scientific analysis has so clearly and usefully taken apart. Then we shall be struck by the necessity in which we shall find ourselves of resorting to the continuous and dominating influence of an 'inventive – that is to say psychic – power' as a *physical* explanation both of the constant upward movement of elementary terms to build always more mechanically improbable groups; and, in the course of this upward movement, the astonishing expansions of spontaneity that we witness.

Among these expansions, one particularly, that of humanity, (the last in time) is absolutely extraordinary, and seems fated (once we decide to study it scientifically without prejudice and by the same right as other phenomena in the world) to give us the key to and direction of evolution. It is very possible, as we have said, that the human branch is attached historically, in some way, to the general primate trunk. But when, starting from the fact of this possible connection, we try to see man as merely a primate *like the others*, we close our eyes to the *greatest of the phenomena* that science can have recorded since the condensation of matter and the first appearance of life: we mean the appearance, extension and definite establishment on earth of the power of thought.[1]

[1] To deal with the grossly ambiguous statement of so many textbooks that 'man descends from the simians', it is as well, therefore, to avoid all discussion of the

Energies of a psychic nature everywhere control the development of life; and man by his thought has renewed the face of the earth.

The more one considers these two categories of facts, the more convinced one feels that transformism, far from reducing the mind that accepts its theories to materialism, must on the contrary incline it to admit the *primacy of spiritual energies* in the universe.

2. Now, this primacy once admitted in the intellectual sphere, what follows *in the realm of practical life*?

In the field of morals, even more than in that of thought, it has been repeated that transformist theories corrupt and are the cause of all our ills. This complaint is perhaps just if one understands evolution in a materialist sense. But, if one takes it, as we have just said, spiritually, then the accusation no longer holds. For anyone who sees the universe in the form of a laborious common ascent towards the greatest consciousness, life, far from seeming blind, harsh or contemptible, assumes a new seriousness, new responsibilities and new connections. As Sir Oliver Lodge very justly wrote, not long ago: 'Rightly understood, the theory of evolution offers us a lesson of hope'.[1] Let us add that it teaches us greater mutual charity and greater effort also.

So, along the whole line, one can defend the following unparadoxical thesis, undoubtedly the best guide and comfort for those confronting the rising wave of transformist views: Transformism does not necessarily open the road to an invasion of spirit by matter; it testifies, rather, on the side of an essential triumph of spirit. Evolution is as capable as the theory of fixed species, if not more so, of investing the universe with that greatness, depth and unity which are the natural climate of Christian faith.

---

[1] I have not found Sir Oliver Lodge's original words, and have therefore reconstructed them from the perhaps somewhat free French version. – Transl.

---

fact, which is hard to deny, of some biological connection between man and the rest of the animal world. Basing ourselves on the facts, we must dilate on the empirical characteristics that make man into a new realm of nature, a new 'creation'. No matter, indeed, how man was born provided his transcendence is assured.

And this last reflection leads us to conclude with the following general remark. Whatever we Christians may say on the subject of transformism or of any other of the general views that attract modern thought, let us never give the impression that we are afraid of something which may renew and enlarge our ideas of man and the universe. The world will never be vast enough, nor will humanity ever be strong enough to be worthy of Him who created them and incarnated Himself in them.

Revue des Questions Scientifiques, January 1930.

CHAPTER XI

THE PHENOMENON OF MAN

By the expression 'The Phenomenon of Man' we mean here the empirical fact of the appearance in our universe of the power of reflexion and thought. For enormous periods the earth certainly lacked any real manifestation of life. Then for another enormous period in the layer of organic matter which appeared on its solid or watery envelope, it presented only signs of spontaneity, and unreflective consciousness (the animal feels and perceives; but he does not appear to know that he feels and perceives). Finally, in a relatively recent epoch, automatism and consciousness acquired on earth, in the zone of life that had become human, the property of isolating and individualizing themselves in their own sight. Man knows that he knows. He emerges from his actions. He dominates them in however feeble a way. He can therefore abstract, combine and foresee. He reflects. He thinks. This event can serve as a point of departure for many philosophical, moral or religious trains of thought. We would only view it here, at least preliminarily, as a simple point in history and science.[1] For a very long time there was no thought on earth. Now there is, and to such a degree, that the face of things is entirely changed. Now we are really viewing a purely scientific fact, a phenomenon. What are we to think of this phenomenon?

It is an extraordinary thing. Scientists, for the last hundred years have been examining, with unheard of subtlety and daring, the mysteries of material atoms and the living cell. They have weighed the electron and the stars. They have dissected hundreds of thousands of specimens of the vegetable and animal world. They are striving with

[1] I would remark that our viewpoint here is purely methodological. Taking up our position in the field of pure empirical science, we rule out, without in any way denying, the revealed knowledge, which is richer and more exact, afforded us by the Catholic faith.

infinite patience to link the human form anatomically to that of the other vertebrates. Passing more directly to the study of our zoological type, they endeavour to examine the springs of human psychology, or to isolate the laws governing the exchanges of products and services in the growing complexity of our society. Now in the midst of these great labours, almost nobody has yet decided to put the main question: 'But what exactly is the phenomenon of man?' That is to say, in rather more precise terms: 'What is the place and purpose of this extraordinary power of thought in the development of the world of experience?' Let us repeat: Man today is scientifically known and recognized by a great number of detailed properties or connections. But, perhaps because some are afraid of lapsing into metaphysics and others of desecrating the 'soul' by treating it as a simple physical object, man, in his special and most revealing characteristics, that is to say in what are called his 'spiritual' properties is still left out of our general pictures of the world. Hence this paradoxical fact: there is a science of the universe without man. There is also a science of man as marginal to the universe; but there is not yet a science of the universe that embraces man as such. Present-day physics (taking this word in the broad Greek sense of a 'systematic understanding of all nature') does not yet give a place to thought; which means that it still exists in complete independence of the most remarkable phenomenon exposed by nature to our observation.

We should like, in these pages, to combat this very anti-scientific situation by sketching in very broad outline the possible features of a universe in which the specifically human characteristics (reflexion and thought) will be introduced as a sort of new dimension. This attempt is of course quite provisional. It is in danger of appearing to some a poetic invention rather than a system of solidly assembled facts. But who can say that an attractive harmony may not to some extent be the birth-charm and precursor of a stricter truth?[1]

[1] The reader will note that the scientific ideas here propounded are in perfect agreement with the Catholic dogma of the special creation of human souls. The supernatural destinies of the human race, and of each man in particular, explain and expand for the believer the effective goal to which life is progressing.

A *Characteristics of the Phenomenon of Man*

The importance of the human milieu escapes us because we are immersed in it. Born in it and breathing nothing else, we have difficulty in getting a just impression of its dimensions, of sensing its extraordinary qualities.

Before we can even suspect its more interesting features, we must first make the difficult effort of mentally taking ourselves out of it. Nothing better prepares the mind, indeed, to perceive the phenomenon of man, than to practise the sciences which seek to reconstruct the general history of the earth. Humanity seems small and tiresome beside the great forces of nature. But let us forget it for a time and fix our eyes on the dim and distant ages in which our planet moved without appearance of life or thought. Let us follow geology, palaeontology. We cast our eyes on the world around us. If we have actually been able to relive the past a little, we shall receive an intellectual shock when we suddenly become aware of the fact that, by our individual existence, we are now situated in a place and time in which one of the fundamental currents of the universe is moving with surprising power into a newly opened domain.

1. *Power of the phenomenon of man.* The power of the phenomenon of man can be measured by the way in which it has succeeded in a relatively short time in establishing itself and covering the earth. Up to the beginning of what is called the Quaternary age (let us say, to get a rough idea, about four or five hundred thousand years ago, perhaps a little more) nothing seems to prophesy the incursion of thought except a gradual ascent of instinct towards those suppler and richer forms that we recognize in the simian anthropomorphs. Man is perhaps already there; but we cannot distinguish him. And then, in a period so brief that, transferred to the ancient geological eras it would not count at all, everything changes. A first hardly noticeable wave leaving rare remains such as the Pithecanthropus of Java, the Peking Sinanthropus and Heidelberg man. A second, stronger, covering the

163

ancient world with very ancient stone implements. A third, giving rise among some survivors of preceding ages (Neanderthal man) to the present day group, fully formed, of *Homo sapiens* (Whites, Yellows and Blacks, all at the same time). A fourth, in Neolithic times, marking the definite conquest of the whole earth (including America) by an agricultural and trading population. Lastly, a fifth, still in process of growth, which is advancing clamorously towards an extraordinary industrialization and unification of the world. In a few great waves the human tide has swept away or submerged all the rest of life. What the lower vertebrates, then the reptiles, then the mass of mammals had slowly and incompletely achieved of old – that is to say the invasion of the whole earth – man has accomplished alone in a few thousand years, and in a way that is both new and prodigious. Not only does he today penetrate everywhere and occupy all inhabitable places; but within the immense sheets that he throws over the world he establishes an organized cohesion of which nothing before him even suggested an idea. By multiplying communications and rapid exchanges, and even more by harnessing the ether, man has reached the state (still in full progress) that individuals, living closer and closer together, tend to permeate one another vitally – at the cost of some explosions, as we know! It has been remarked that, seen from very far away, the earth, covered with its plants and oceans, must appear green and blue. To a distant observer, able to make it out more clearly, it would appear at this moment luminous with thought. From the most coldly positivist viewpoint, the phenomenon of man represents at the very least a general transformation of the earth by the establishment on its surface of a new envelope, the thinking envelope; more vibrant and a better conductor, in a sense, than any metal; more fluid than any liquid; more expansive than any gas; more assimilative and more sensitive than all organic matter. And what gives this metamorphosis its full grandeur is that it did not take place as a secondary event or a chance accident, but in the form of a crisis, prepared in essence from the beginning, by the very play of the general evolution of the world.[1]

[1] Clearly inspired by the Creator.

2. *Deep and central origins of the phenomenon of man*. We must not, indeed, let ourselves be taken in by the inevitable simplifications of textbooks, or even large books of palaeontology and zoology. In these works, for which morphology (the study of forms) is the principal object of research, the value of vital changes is principally measured by their osteological effects: a modification in limb structure assumes as much importance as a larger brain. So, the phylogeny of horses, for example, seems an equivalent phenomenon to the phylogeny of man. This confusion of levels must be scrupulously corrected if we are to attain a correct view of the whole of living phenomena; for nothing is more essential to an exact knowledge of the world (as to any work of art or truth) than to discover and respect the true proportions of things. Though often placed on the same level, the various lines of zoological development recognized by zoology are in reality very uneven in their value or order. In a tree there are leaves, twigs, boughs, main branches; and then there is also the principal axis of growth, the leading shoot. Similarly, in the complicated edifice of animal lines of which the whole constitutes the group of living beings, we must distinguish beneath the frondage or bushiness of countless different forms (each corresponding to a different mode of activity or nutrition) a fundamental line of growth and a sort of peak. The fundamental line of growth – one becomes progressively less able to avoid this almost direct evidence – is the advance of organic beings towards a growth of spontaneity and consciousness. The kind of peak – it would be childish to deny this out of fear of some kind of 'anthropomorphism' – is, at this present moment, man. Man, no doubt, can be defined on the non-relief map of systematics as a family of primates recognizable by certain details of skull, pelvis and limbs – exactly as the leading shoot of the tree about which we were just speaking can always be distinguished by some details of the adjoining branches if we do not take into account its position in the plant-complex which it dominates. But if we wish to place it in a truly natural picture of the world, which takes into account the whole evolution of life, its principal definition must be by its property of 'taking the lead' at this moment in the movement drawing

organic beings towards greater possibilities of knowledge and action. Similarly, before man's arrival, the entire line of higher primates already occupied a place apart in nature. But man, by his arrival, swept them aside, making so decisive an advance over everything around him that he is now alone in the lead. It is not enough, in fact, to have recognized, as we have just done, that the phenomenon of man at present marks the advanced front of life. Fully to appreciate it, we have still to realize that his appearance marks an absolutely new phase on this same line of propagation.

3. *Critical character of the phenomenon of man.* This is, in fact, the only scientific phrase capable of expressing the revolutionary metamorphosis signalled by man's appearance on the face of the earth. With man, the hitherto even development of life has reached a *critical point*. With man the general movement of organized beings towards consciousness has passed a major interval. Carrying, as he still appears to do, in his hereditary organism, features accumulated in the course of previous phases, which still allow zoologists to class him as a primate, man has inaugurated a new sphere on earth, the sphere of rational discovery, of artificial constructions and of an organized totality. Between man and all that preceded him, there is a change of state, a break. Here, expressed as scientifically as possible, is the fundamental fact that has too often been rejected or ignored because no one has dared to state it in the simple form in which it appears; with the result that the world's symmetries have been distorted and its clarity obscured. A good number of thinkers and scientists systematically exclude humanity from their theories as an anomaly, under the pretext that it seems to belong to 'a different order of knowledge' from the phenomena they are in the habit of treating. But have we not known for a long time that the true advances of science consist precisely in discovering the hidden links uniting orders apparently very far apart? Are not the equations of mechanics at this moment becoming one with those of light? And what would have happened to modern physics if radio-activity had been neglected as a strange and inconvenient phenomenon? If the phenomenon of man is to be

made acceptable and allowed to display its rich potentialities for science, the first condition is that we shall not dodge or minimize its implications. Man is an embarrassment to science only because it hesitates to accept him at his full significance, that is to say as the appearance, at the goal of a continuous transformation, of an absolutely new state of life. Let us recognize frankly, once and for all, that in any realistic picture of world history, the coming to power of thought is as real, specific and great an event as the first condensation of matter or the first appearance of life: and we shall perhaps see, instead of the disorder we feared, a more perfect harmony pervading our pictures of the universe.

B *Interpretation of the Phenomenon of Man*

The ideas expressed above concerning the existence and principal characteristics of the phenomenon of man seem indisputable. Those that follow will perhaps appear, as we have already said, more poetic than scientific. They have at least the advantage of presenting a general and logical view of the world.

As a point of departure for this new development, we will take the well-established fact that the whole collection of known physical phenomena is governed by the extremely general law of entropy, that is to say by the decline or diminution of utilizable energy. In the course of all work, thermodynamics states, part of the energy is dissipated in the form of irrecoverable heat. The power of action of the material universe is therefore gradually diminishing. In the atomic world-pictures today accepted by science on positive proof, this great phenomenon of the evening out of cosmic energy is explained as a statistical effect. The utilizable energy of the universe being dependent on a heterogeneous distribution of corpuscular elements (heterogeneity producing 'differences of potential'), the play of probabilities tends inexorably to bring these elements to a *more probable*,[1] that is to say homogeneous distribution, in which powers of action are

[1] The relationship of these ideas to those lately presented by Professor E. Le Roy in his lectures at the Collège de France will immediately be recognized.

neutralized and annulled in a kind of universal tepidity. What is most remarkable about entropy (besides its general application) is that it is not, properly speaking, a law like the rest, expressing absolute conditions of equilibrium at a given moment. It expresses a universal tendency of material phenomena throughout time. It explains a historical current as an algebraical formula: the advance of matter towards the most probable conditions and arrangements. In this way it acts as a bridge between mathematical physics and the natural sciences.

Having made this statement, let us leave entropy for a moment and return to living creatures. In terms of physics and chemistry, the phenomena of life are essentially characterized (in precise contrast to those of matter) by an evolution towards the *least probable*. Improbabilities in the huge and unstable molecules accumulated by organic matter; improbabilities in the incredibly complicated structure of the smallest protozoon; improbabilities of a rapidly increasing order in the formation of the higher animals and their development into various and progressive types throughout the geological ages; finally, the supreme improbabilities of the appearance, conservation and organization of thought on earth. Man is supported by a giddy scaffolding of improbabilities, to which each new progress adds a new platform.

Faced with the huge and undeniable fact of the regular ascent of a part of the world towards states of increasing improbability, science has hitherto tried to close or turn away its eyes. If life's productions are improbable, then they are fortuitous and uninteresting material for speculation and calculation. And life continues to remain outside physics as an aberration: a strange counter-current arising by accident in the sole primitive and definitive stream of entropy.

Now might there not be another possible picture, arising automatically from the simplest words we can discover in which to express our experiences of the universe? If, in the universe, we find ourselves confronted with two important movements of elementary unities, one towards the more probable and one towards the less, why not try to find in this dual current two phenomena of the same general nature, importance and order: two aspects or two directions of a single, extremely general event?

Why, in fact, should not life be a counterpart or inverse of entropy? Clearly, if we are to raise life to the dignity of a second fundamental world current, there are two drawbacks to be overcome: its apparent spatial limitation and extreme fragility. How, it will be objected, can we compare to the huge and irresistible movements of cosmic energy the thin and unstable layer of constructive spontaneities with which our small earth has enveloped itself as a result of an improbable series of chances? We hesitate to weigh objects of such manifestly different sizes in the same scales. But is not this merely because we have not sufficiently understood the lessons of the phenomenon of man?

For so long as life remains enveloped in its 'instinctive' forms, one can more or less feasibly try to reduce it to simple mechanisms. But in man it explodes with properties most certainly irreducible to the laws of the physics it observes and utilizes. In man life, carried forward into thought, shows itself as *sui generis* an aspect of the world's powers. This new energy is narrowly localized in its manifestations: but the history of its preparation and success seems co-extensive with the entire evolution of matter. It is true that it appears ridiculously weak; but the sure steps by which it has continuously advanced towards humanity do not point to the action of simple chance, and therefore escape its dangers. Something as irresistible as matter hides beneath the patient infallibility of the ascent of human kind. We have assumed the rather childish habit of describing the most probable combinations in terms of the ultimate equilibrium, the solidity of the earth. Perhaps we should do better to reverse the scale of our values entirely. Perhaps the true stability, the true consistency of the universe should be looked for in the direction of increased improbability.[1]

[1] It could still be objected against the physical equivalence of life and entropy that life is itself fundamentally governed by entropy since it is built of elements that are subject to the general laws of energy. But are we quite sure that in its completely

In brief, just as the old atomism is accepted and transformed in the syntheses of modern physics so there might be a case for making a scientific examination of the old intuitions of a cosmic dualism. The universe may not be as simple as we think; it may not be gliding down a single slope towards homogeneity and rest. The whole of its primordial excitation may be divisible into two irreversibles. One by the accumulation and conjunction of confused movements might lead to a progressive neutralization and something like disappearance of activities and freedoms; this is entropy. The other, by directed explorations and growing differentiation, might bring a freedom with no scientifically ascertainable limits[1] (but no doubt in the direction of some new change of state analogous to that marked by the appearance of the phenomenon of man) to the truly progressive portion of the world. On the one side great numbers swallowing up unity; on the other unity born of great numbers. All this may be poetry, let us repeat, but it has the virtue of directing us towards certain exact and practical paths of progress.

C   *Applications of the Knowledge of the Phenomenon of Man*

Let us accept, at least as a provisional hypothesis, that in human consciousness one of these two fundamental currents of the universe (the only one of the two of which one can truly say that it has a future)

---

[1] The irreversibility of the stream of life is proved, to a certain degree, by its very success: why should it go back since, as a whole, it has done nothing but grow since its beginnings? One may add (and this proof is very strong if we can understand it) that in the case of man in whom it becomes reflective, life seems to require, for its very functioning, that it shall be irreversible. In fact if we should ever discover that the animate universe is moving towards total death, the desire to act would be killed, *ipso facto* in our hearts; that is to say that by becoming conscious of itself, life would destroy itself. And this seems absurd.

---

vitalized radius (weak though this radius is) animate matter still dissipates energy in order to act? Let us not forget that the laws of physics are only valid for large numbers. Now the specifically living action of a living being (individual or collective) is essentially an isolated action, the action of a single element.

reflects upon itself and to some degree achieves consciousness and mastery of itself. What effect has this on our power of understanding and action?

For our understanding of the world, we find, first of all, that we possess a marvellous means of exploration *from within*. Let us observe ourselves; and we shall find, by intuition if not by calculation, something of all the past movements of the universe in the living creatures we are. Let us join and exalt our individual powers; and we shall glimpse the grandeur towards which the phenomenon of man is progressing. Let us then narrow our possibilities of perception and choice: and we find ourselves back on the dark roads that life climbed, up to thought, by way of a long series of instinctive 'inventions'. Lastly, let us observe the veil of determinism which tends incessantly to conceal the repetition and disorganized multitude of our actions: and we catch in the act, in this invasion of our being by the tendency to greater probability, a true birth of matter. Once more there is nothing measurable in this. But though figures have an indisputable value for precision and construction, it does not follow that no empirical knowledge can have speculative and practical value without them. We have just glanced at the horizons revealed by this interpretation of the facts; we see how this interpretation of man fills our need for understanding. Let us now see what impetus and direction it brings, scientifically, to our need for action.

The impetus is that it shows us a need for action which is at once vast and tangible. One has no need to be a great scholar to perceive that the greatest danger which may frighten humanity is not some external catastrophe or famine or plague, but rather that spiritual sickness (the most terrible because the most directly antihuman of all scourges), the loss of appetite for living. As he becomes increasingly conscious of himself by reflexion, man sees himself confronted in an increasingly acute form, with the problem of the value of action. By his existence he finds himself engaged, by no wish of his own, in a vast system of activities that demands a perpetual effort of him. What does this compulsion mean? Are we chosen or are we dupes? Is life a road or a blind alley? This is the question, scarcely formulated a few centuries ago, which is now explicit and on all men's lips. Following the short and violent crisis in which it became conscious simultaneously of its creative powers and its critical faculties, humanity has become rightfully awkward; and no spur drawn from the instincts or blind economic needs will suffice for long to drive it forward. Only one motive, one true and important motive, a passionate love of life, will decide it to move any further. But where, on the empirical plane, can we find the bait (if not the actuality) of a justification for life? Nowhere else, it seems, but in the consideration of the intrinsic value of the phenomenon of man. Continue to consider man an accidental outgrowth or toy in the world of things; and you drive him to a disgust or revolt which, if they were to become general, would cause a definite check to life on earth. Recognize, on the other hand, that in the realm of our experience man, because he is the advancing front of one of the two most enormous waves into which tangible reality is for us divided, holds the fate of the universe in his hands: and you turn his face towards the great rising sun. So long as he feels lost and isolated in the mass of things man has every reason to feel disturbed about himself. But once he discovers that his fate is linked with that of nature herself, then he should leap joyfully forward. For to suspect a whole world's values and hopes would not be the virtue of a critic but a spiritual disease.[1] In fact, without waiting for science to be 'converted', our generation has understood the profound significance of its fate. In us and around us, almost beneath our eyes, a psychological phenomenon of great magnitude is developing (born hardly a century ago!) which might be called: *the awakening of the sense of humanity*. In a positive sense, men began to feel themselves bound together, all united in a great task, and captivated, in an almost religious sense, by its progress. To know more, to be able to do more. Although many still take these words in a utilitarian sense, for the great majority they are already tinged with sacred value. In our days people constantly devote their lives to 'the progress of the world'. Thus in actions more substantial than any speculation

[1] Cf. note 1, p. 170.

they show their implicit recognition of the phenomenon of man. Along what lines should this movement, by its very nature, seek to continue?

The principal points of the programme are as clear and precise as the conditions regulating the use and growth of any kind of energy. They are these:

(*a*) First and foremost, to watch over the maintenance and growth in the human mass of the urge for life, the appetite for living: a more precious potential than any reserve of coal or oil. For this purpose we must begin by reducing the numerous and inexcusable leaks, which take place everywhere in modern society in the form of disordered actions and wasted love. And to do so, we must above all develop our perception and appreciation of the great universal realities, feed our sense of the world and our sense of humanity. It remains to be seen (this is no place to discuss the question) whether such a faith in the universe, by exacting a guaranteed and as if absolute goal, will not end in the recognition and adoration of God.

(*b*) This human urge towards the best once safeguarded, it must then be directed towards truly progressive ends. The general formula for this useful work can be reduced to a single word: *unify*. To unify the elements by perfecting each personality, nature's masterpiece, within itself. And to unify the whole by favouring and regularizing the affinities which tend so clearly at the present day to group all human unities into a sort of single organ of conquest and research.

Thus, the physical laws governing the progress of the stream of 'improbability' in the universe inevitably express themselves, on man's level, in terms of morality and religion.

Morality and religion appear absolutely foreign to physics (and even to biology) in a cosmos reduced to a single realm of laws of probability and high numbers. One great surprise awaiting those who seek firmly to place man among the phenomena, is that they will find both morality and religion assuming the dual role of energy and structure over the complete earth, and both closely concerned with the true conservation and progress of the universe.

The advance of human knowledge (these shall be the last words of this brief inquiry) seems decidedly to be moving towards a state in which the various departments of empirical science having gradually come together, there will remain only a single natural science centred on man the knower and man the object of knowledge.[1]

Revue des Questions Scientifiques, November 1930.

---

[1] The idea is in the air, everywhere. Thus in the *Literary Digest* of June 21, 1930, (p. 30), we read this sentence attributed by a reporter to the well-known physicists Compton and Heisenberg: 'We found strong reasons for believing that, in spite of his physical insignificance, man may be of extraordinary importance in the cosmic scheme.'

CHAPTER XII

MAN'S PLACE IN NATURE

As Professor O. Abel recently observed, it is with some surprise that we discover on reopening Linnaeus, at his chapter on man, at least a verbal likeness between his language and ours. In the great Swedish scientist's classification of beings, not only is man placed as a simple genus among the primates; but within this genus a place is made for the species champanzee! Except for a few details, does this not already state the present position of science? That is to say, have we not gone through a great deal of movement in the last hundred and fifty years to end up where we began?

This impression may affect our minds for an instant. It requires no more than a further instant for reflexion to see its vanity. No, there is no identity between our conceptions of man, as they are affirmed today, and the views of the eighteenth-century natural scientists; they are a world apart, just as our present ideas will, perhaps, be a world apart from those in process of being born around us.

What has been done in the course of the last century to determine man's place in nature? And what remains to be done? I should like to suggest the answer in this short study.

A *The Progress Attained*

The great intellectual event which will in the future mark the nineteenth century is not so much man's conquest, by means of physics and chemistry, of the energies of matter, as the discovery, by the scientists and thinkers together, of time and evolution. Extraordinary though this may appear, the universe has not always seemed to man

to be vast and in motion. We have only to go three or four generations back to find a society whose world picture would defeat and
stifle us by its limitations, fixity and disjointedness. Until the end of
the eighteenth century, the earth was still thought of as a world only
some thousands of years old; a world whose elements appeared suddenly ready made, and already possessed of their present forms; a
world whose internal relationships express a purely ideal plan to the
exclusion of all organic connections. Today, at the conclusion of an
intellectual revolution much greater than the revolution in astronomy at the time of Galileo, the whole appearance of beings in
nature has changed to our eyes. Below and behind us, the unbounded
abyss of time has opened; and our picture of the world before us is
now that of a temporary stage in an immense genesis (or one might
say embryogenesis).

There is not a single department of empirical science in which the
appearance of the evolutionary theory has not modified our views
(in the same way as the introduction of a new dimension modifies a
geometrical figure). But nowhere has the alteration of values been
so profound as in the realm of living beings. For Linnaeus the various
divisions of systematics (orders, families, kinds, species) represented
abstract categories: ideal curves written into the plan of creation.
For us this distribution has come to indicate in nature the various
streams of life that have separated, then grown big, then spread in the
course of ages. The greater or less proximity observed between two
zoological forms denotes the closer or more distant relationship of
these forms in the evolutionary pattern. The natural classification of
beings expresses their genealogy: that is the ray of light. If man is a
primate, therefore, it is because he appeared *on the stem* of primates
among the many branches of vertebrates. Such is the enormous and
essential change that words have undergone since the time of Linnaeus. The words are the same, the meaning different. Intellectually
to accept the possibility, and scientifically to demonstrate the reality
of this *birth* of man in the midst of general life has been one of the
finest achievements of man's persistence and tenacity in the course of
the last years.

As always happens in the history of great scientific revolutions, the mind at first advanced more quickly than events in the recognition of zoological evolution and its extension to man. Comparative anatomy alone already spoke quite clearly to those who could understand. But positive historical documents from archives dating back to geological times were at first missing; in other words, advocates of transformism had no fossils by which to prove the correctness of their views (often expressed, it must be admitted, in a confused or over-simplified way). It was not until the second half of the nineteenth century that palaeontology could begin to trace at all boldly the filiations of a few living forms. Since then, our knowledge of vanished species and their mutual connections has progressed beyond all our hopes. One after another, the most isolated forms we know in present-day nature (the elephant, the camel, the whale, etc) have been linked in the depths of time to mighty groups which converged in their turn towards the base. The distant history of the primates and their relationship with the most primitive mammals of the Tertiary were also laid bare. By this irresistible descent of the whole living world in evolution, the empirical problem of the zoological origins of man was already virtually resolved. Even if we had not yet found a human fossil, the birth of man from pre-human forms would already be certain from what we have learnt about the universal derivation of all living beings from other living beings.

But there, of course, direct indications or proofs had still to be found. Hence arose the science of prehistory. Its mere name would have disconcerted our fathers. But its extraordinarily rapid progress – it is still not eighty years old – has amply justified it and promises still greater advances in the future.

It is the same with prehistory as with wireless and aeroplanes. We cannot imagine that it has not always existed. And yet it is scarcely more than a generation ago that the Institut de France refused to admit the possibility of chipped flints in the old terraces of the Somme; and the finding of an incised mammoth tooth, a conclusive proof that man lived in the company of this extinct animal, was considered sensational. How far we have come since then! In western Europe, there is the discovery of Neanderthal man, the last and best-known representative of true fossil man. In Java the discovery of Pithecanthropus; then in Germany of Heidelberg man; then, last of all, of Sinanthropus at Peking; which bring us right into the middle and even into the beginnings of the Pleistocene. There had been discoveries, more abundant because much easier, of chipped stones, which outline the successive phases, geographical divisions and enormous extension of the first civilizations, stretching through the Quaternary, of the entire Old World. We know that we are only at the beginning of our researches. And yet already the essential lines of the *Human Fact* stand out before our eyes in growing relief. First, more distant and at greater depths than we can clearly make out, the first sheet: humanity of the lower Palaeolithic (Pithecanthropus, Heidelberg man, Sinanthropus) an obscure group of beings with dominant Neanderthaloid characteristics, of which nothing remains today except heavily fossilized remains. Then, already much nearer, and suddenly sweeping away the last remains of Mousterian man, the wave of the upper Palaeolithic (Whites, Yellows and Blacks like us), simple hunters still, but already practising art. Then the Neolithic revolution: man grouping himself in large social and agricultural units, and finding in this organization the power to expand right across the world (including America). Then after what seems to us a disproportionate interval, but which is far the shortest of the three, the present revolution: the era of industry and great international undertakings – a powerfully based yet almost newborn wave which is lifting and carrying us forward to new states.

Man, placed in the general evolution of life, of which he is one of the extensions; the human group then itself becoming subject to an internal evolution which can be detected in its osteological structure but appears to concentrate increasingly in the psychic and social zones. Such are the two fundamental views revealed to us since the time of Linnaeus by the combined efforts of palaeontology, prehistory and anthropology. And now, from what directions can we expect still further light?

B *Progress to be Hoped for*

The field at present open to a science of man extending far beyond the old anthropology cannot yet be shown in detail. The programme of researches clearly involves in the first place the consolidation and extension of the positions conquered. To speak only of the three oldest epochs of prehistory, we most clearly need those remains of Sinanthropus and Heidelberg man; our knowledge must be based on more complete skulls and skeletons. By wider and more precise investigations, we must try to locate the probable region in which the mysterious 'hominization' of the last pre-men took place. Was it in Central Asia or on the edge of the tropical forest? Is there, in man's case, a single site, or a broadly extensive zone (or front) of evolution? It will be more and more important to isolate and clearly pose these various problems, in order to undertake concerted and methodical researches at the 'sensitive points' of the earth.[1]

But even so, this is only the simple continuation of work already begun. May there not be, in the study of man, not only furrows to be prolonged but also a door to be opened on new horizons? I think there is; and this marvellous door would be, in my opinion, a better comprehension of what may be called the *specific phenomenon of man*.

What characterizes, as I have just explained, the work of the anthropological sciences during the last years is the effort to relate man's case to that of the other living beings by proving that his appearance too was subject to the general laws of evolution. The search for the organic link, for the element of continuity, the 'phylum', has therefore dominated all researches in anthropology, as it has also dominated all the other biological sciences. Let us not forget that, having only just discovered evolution, we have been so fascinated by the continuity of its curve that we have not thought that its greatness and interest might have another side: that it might also reveal to us certain regions of discontinuity. Pushed to a certain degree of convergence, the surfaces of a cone fuse at a point of no magnitude. Raised

[1] Cf. Teilhard de Chardin: *The Appearance of Man*, Chap. XVI: 'Africa and Human Origins.'

to a certain temperature or submitted to a certain pressure, bodies *change state*; they liquefy or vaporize. There are everywhere 'critical or 'singular' points in the movements of matter. Why should there not be some such points in the transformations of life? In fact the phenomena of discontinuity have tended for some time to assume an increasing importance in the evolutionary theories of nature. On a tiny scale, de Vries's mutations are a first type of discontinuity. But other, more extensive mutations reveal themselves speculatively at the origin of the great phyla (tetrapods, amphibians, mammals, etc). Should not the first birth of organic matter be interpreted as a major discontinuity occurring in the course of a process begun in pre-life? One great fact that yesterday's anthropology did not see owing to its excessive preoccupation with 'missing links' will in my opinion illuminate the anthropology of tomorrow; and this is that the appearance in the world of the *power of thought* (that is to say a being's power of reflecting on himself) is also to be understood as a discontinuity of the first order, comparable with the first appearance of organic beings. Man is a thinking animal: a banal expression if thought is understood as a sort of secondary property, accidentally superimposed on life (as when Linnaeus said that man is a primate); but an expression charged with serious consequences if the same word is understood, as it should be in sound evolutionary theory, to denote an axial and higher form of life.

Let us observe the profound changes that took place in our world when thought broke into flower and we shall recognize as clearly as in the case of other scientific truth that with man, it was not only one more species characterized by certain details of the skull and limbs, appearing in the crowd of others; it was *a new state of life* manifesting itself in nature. Thought is an actual physical energy *sui generis*, which has succeeded in a few hundred centuries in covering the entire face of the earth with a network of linked forces. It must therefore receive a place of its own in our theories. This is the opinion of scholars who, with my friend Dr. Grabau, support the idea that in the Quaternary, a new era opened, the *Psychozoic*; an era comparable in importance, despite its recent date, to the greatest periods of past life. It is understood in this sense by those philosophers also who, following Professor E. Le Roy (Bergson's successor at the Collège de France), claim to distinguish, haloing the biosphere of the great geologist Suess, the thinking layer of the earth, or 'Noosphere'. This would undoubtedly be the opinion also of scholars on any other planet (supposing them to exist), if they were in the position to know what is happening to our world.

With man and in man life has passed over a threshold. Here, open before us, is the door of which we were just speaking. Since the birth of science we have sounded sidereal space, the oceans and mountains. Let us now turn at last to the mysterious stream of consciousness of which we form a part. *Thought has never yet been studied* in the same way as the immensities of matter, *as a reality of cosmic and evolutionary nature.* Let us take this step. Let us accept the reality, analyse the properties and determine the place of the phenomenon of man in the general history of the world. Two great consequences, one theoretical, the other practical, come into sight as a result of the exploration of this new field.

From the theoretical point of view, the fact of recognizing in man a new property (or more exactly we should say a new state) of life, would help us finally to discover an absolute direction, a pole in the great movements and in life's heavens. Left to itself, pure zoology is powerless to provide us with a guiding thread in the labyrinth of living forms of which the biosphere is woven. Is it a true progress or simply a diversification that leads from the protozoon to the dinosaur and the primate? Yes, the science of man may one day decide, it is a true progress; for in the persistent advance of consciousness towards always more spontaneous and finally reflective forms, we have an objective element, allowing us to follow, through and beneath all complications of detail, the continually ascending advance of a single fundamental greatness. A consciousness gradually waking by way of countless fumblings, this would, in this case, be the essential picture of evolution.

If it is true then that the terrestrial evolution of life concentrates and emerges in man in its temporarily most finished form, everyone must see the practical consequences. Up to now our science has principally consisted of an examination of man's past. Will it not find itself led henceforth principally to look for means of assuring his *future*? The inner movement of the world, in its most central and most living form, today passes through us. We represent the present front of the wave. What shall we do, since we are its conscious elements, to help its advance? What organizations shall we choose? What relations shall we form between peoples? What roads shall we open up. What morality adopt? Towards what ideal collect our energies? By what hope preserve in the heart of the human mass the sacred appetite for research and progress?

The immense virtue of the founders of anthropology was that they rediscovered the historic links organically binding man to life and the earth. But their work will only bear fruit when man, now conscious by their aid of his consanguinity with the universe, understands that it is his fate in himself to sublimate and save the spirit of the earth and of life.

Not only to recognize evolution, but to make it continue in ourselves.

Revue des étudiants de l'Université Nationale de Péking, 1932.

Editorial note: Father Teilhard says of this essay in a letter to his cousin: 'Father Maréchal of Louvain pays me the compliment of writing: "No one today has a mastery like yours of all the theological, philosophical and scientific facts about the problem of evolution"' (*Letters from a Traveller*, p. 206).

CHAPTER XIII

THE DISCOVERY OF THE PAST

A *The Expansion of Consciousness*

In a biologist's or philosopher's eyes, one problem eclipses all others on earth at present, that of the expansion of consciousness.

To catalogue everything, test everything, understand everything. What is above, higher than the air we breathe; what is below, deeper than light can penetrate. What is lost in sidereal space and what the elements conceal. Air, ocean, earth, ether, matter. Thought filters through empirical reality, impelled by a pressure that nothing can stop. Some realms deemed for ever impenetrable. Do not rely on that! One machine replaces another, each more ambitious than the last. One after another, men die. But consciousness progresses. It can no more be stopped than heat can be stopped from passing through iron.

The instinct which has drawn so many seekers in recent times towards the discovery of the past clearly connects with this general expansion of the spirit as a special sense.

For a long time, the past must have seemed to men a definitely vanished (and, moreover, narrow) tract of the universe, a lost country of which they could not know much more than was preserved by oral traditions and a few old books.

But now, little by little, thanks principally to geology, a scientific method has been developed allowing us to discover and analyse, in what is, the traces of what has been. The disposition of our eyes having thus changed, we have become capable of seeing behind us. And thus a gulf of the past which Pascal never suspected has opened beneath our feet. As at the discovery of the microscope and the telescope, as in the early days of spectral analysis and radiation, a wall has just fallen; and behind it a whole department of life has appeared, a virgin field. Sucked in by this empty space, the mind has rushed forward; it is still rushing forward. Thus the science of history was born in all its fullness. The smallest animal crossing a field, the least stone on the ground have become for the natural scientist as distant and as complicated as the light of a star for the astronomer.

So much energy and money are spent today on the exploration of past centuries! So many excavations, reports, museums! So many men who devote the whole of their lives to what existed before us! Why am I myself as I write these lines travelling to the slopes of the Himalayas, where perhaps among folded detritus the remains of a primitive humanity may be buried. What force impels me, once more, towards Asia? Only a wind blowing from our present life back over the abyss of the past.

Why then do I hesitate in my desire for discovery? Why my confessed reluctance to let it carry me away? One cannot fail to know when one's energy is weakening, one's love diminishing. These signs tell me that my devotion to science is not as natural or as complete as it once was. Is it possible that I am getting tired? Or is it not rather (for my enjoyment of the world is intact) that as the cavity created by the opening up of the past is gradually filled, the tide of consciousness whose waves carried me towards the past is beginning to turn. Perhaps the expansion of the mind varies in duration or value according to its direction. And it would be wrong therefore for human energy to persist along a line that is becoming exhausted. The moment has undoubtedly come for history to ask itself the essential question: 'What has there been? What is there still surviving? What will there be so vital tomorrow for us to discover in the past?'

B   *The Attraction of the Past*

The doubt that inspires me to write these pages cannot have touched the minds of the pioneers of history.

When by turning back from the peaks to which time has carried him, man could suddenly see the whole panorama of the ages, he no doubt felt like Columbus gazing on a new continent. All the novelty, the mystery and the boundless hopes of nascent discovery.

The first delight of exploring the past is the refreshment it brings to our minds. It becomes in the long run very tiring always to see around us the same horizons, the same climates, the same animals. To plunge into the past is to visit a wonderland.

As one goes back the scenery and actors change as can never happen on a mere voyage. Some mountains sink into the ocean, others emerge from the middle of plains. And as we cover this new territory, animals appear that are as real as a scientific fact, and as fantastic as a dream. Renewal, wonder, strangeness.

To gaze in order to wonder. But also to gaze in order to possess. A man entering the jungle for the first time is not content just to look. He wants to grasp with his hands and his mind. To hold. It is precisely this instinct for capture that the past satisfies in us, when it has satisfied our need for change. Everything that we call to life from the ashes of cities and the consolidated mud of the earth is a capture that charms our instinct for growth: to capture and understand. For variety and beauty of trophies no hunting is comparable to the pursuits of history.

Hunting I said. But why speak of hunting? In our days at least hunting has become a fiction, a sport, an empty gesture in which the need for pursuit is satisfied free of charge. For the first explorers of the past, on the other hand, the virgin forest into which they ventured was dramatic with possibilities and infinite expectations. Once upon a time, before geography circled the world, a true mystery must have hung over the unknown regions of the earth. Perhaps a divinity dwelt on the summit of some distant peak or at the inaccessible source of a river? For long now we have smiled at such simplicity. But what no journeying in space could possibly reveal, might perhaps be reached by diving into time. Would not the riddle of the universe be solved if we could succeed in discovering the cradle of life? This is, I think (for I have confusedly felt it myself), the secret attraction that actually prompted the pursuit of history. One day, I am convinced, the movement which launched our generation towards the shores of the past will appear like the rush towards an Eldorado whose promise was *final* knowledge. We set out for the past not as amateurs but as conquistadors, to discover the secret of the world, hidden in its origins.

c *The Appearance of the Future*

Now nature is a great deceiver. When we think we have caught her, it is she who is leading us on.

So when, having found a means of analysing the past, men had with long patience collected a multitude of facts, and when with even greater patience they had placed these facts in their natural position in the depths of the ages, then they looked for an assurance that the path they had thus constructed would really give them access to the primitive essence of the world. But something very different met their gaze. Astronomers were astonished when, having correctly distributed the stars in the firmament, they had to admit that sidereal dust formed an immense whirlwind. Investigators of the past were even more astonished to find that from their cleverly ordered animal series emerged the figure of a movement in which they and their science also were contained. For observers of the thin stratum of the present, the *animate world* seems to stay where it is or at least, if it propagates, to do so by diversification, spreading in a non-committal way. But once seen in sufficient depth, this huge mass appeared to be moving *in one direction*. A wave of advancing consciousness fringed the prow of the universe. And this wave, in the realm accessible to our researches, was humanity.

On mature reflection it is doubtful whether there has even been in the history of man a natural event comparable to this discovery of a motion in the world, not merely in some material part of it but throughout the being itself. This idea that the universe, partially expressed in our individual consciousness, continuously sustains a growth in being which increases its quality, is so vast and rich in consequences that we are only just beginning to assimilate it. There is indeed no realm of thought in which this new perspective, which is much more revolutionary than relativity, does not introduce fertile changes. No wind of ether but a wind of consciousness! We were so accustomed to thinking that everything began to exist one fine day, once and for all!

My aim is not to consider the general conditions of this readjustment. What concerns my inquiry is to analyse the effect on history itself of the unexpected result which its activities have brought. Setting out in search of the past, consciousness has unexpectedly discovered the future. Devoting itself to what has finished its life, it met a stream which carried it irresistibly towards what does not yet exist. How will it react to these opposing influences?

D   *The Fading Mirage*

One first result of this appearance of the future is the disappearance of the dawn that we thought we saw glowing behind us. The essential charm of sailing towards the past was, we used to say, the hope of reaching a centre of light. Now the illusion is no longer permissible. As we follow them back, the temporal series grow thinner, blur and finally become confused. At first we could hope that this was due to a chance and remediable fault in our working methods. In reality we had come up against a structural condition of the universe. The rays in whose light we bask do not diverge from the past, but converge towards the future. The sun is rising *ahead*.

These luminous shades that we see floating over the world's beginnings are therefore reflections from ahead.

And that feeling of newness which overcame us as we explored the secret of vanished things is a reflection also.

In a sense past centuries contain no mystery, and have nothing to give us. The past is left behind.

So any attitude explicitly or implicitly attributing an absolute value to the backward glance is condemned beyond appeal. The pleasure of calling ancient civilizations and vanished worlds back to life is deceptive. The tendency to transfer ourselves intellectually or emotionally into the past, to readopt the framework, art and thought of former times, is biologically false. Our nostalgia for the snows of yesteryear is morbid. What has been has now no intrinsic interest. Forward!

Forward! But then what remains valid in the enthusiasm that drove us for a while to the conquest of the ever more remote past? Can it be that by the discovery of our drift towards the future, history has killed the intrinsic urge that gave it life? Like a plant, must it die when it bears its fruit? I now understand the initial hesitation which vaguely disturbed me and led me to risk these pages. Logically, what remains that can give an evolutionist any vital interest in the investigation of the past?

E *The Residual Tasks of History*

I am forced to confess that, for my own part, since the existence of a growth of the world's being seems scientifically established, any pleasure there may be in deciphering the earth's archives diminishes. What more can we ask of dead things than evidence of the possibilities of progress still open to life? And yet I must confess also that despite certain signs of slowing down, the backward expansion of human consciousness is still too powerful for us to be able to see it as a simple play of inertia. In that direction we are still doing something better than merely running back on our tracks. Once the future exists, what is there for us still to discover in the past?

The task still incumbent on explorers of the past seems to me first of all to consolidate the position we have just occupied. The breakthrough towards the future has indeed been made. But it must be explained. For every man who has understood the profound lessons of history there are still many dozens who still preserve the old illusions. We need proofs, still more proofs of the movement drawing us forward. This is what we require for the final success of our attack. The establishment of a new viewpoint is not an instantaneous illumination, quick as lightning. I have been able to say in all truth that the future has already definitely appeared before us. But in truth also it must be added that this new star is not yet entirely above our horizon. The acquisition of a sense of the future is a biological phenomenon which has its own time. Perhaps it will take many generations for it to extend to its total objective, humanity. And throughout this period, the work of the geologists, of palaeontology and prehistory must be maintained.

So much for the basic work. But there are many subsidiary tasks as well. The true function of history, as we now feel, is to provide a sufficient thickness of the present for the experiments of science. The present, in the common sense of the word, is a layer extremely thin in duration. Very short wave-motions leave their mark on it. Long rhythms, on the other hand, do not make a clear impression, and the rare singularities escape it altogether. Observed in a shallow sheet water seems transparent. And taken in a very small segment, any curve may well appear straight. It is because they have, as we have seen above, managed to construct a very thick layer of the present, that natural scientists have accidentally brought into view the displacement of the universe through consciousness. By the use of this same method, there are probably other great advances to be made in the analysis of the energies inspiring and drawing us forward *now*. Many essential features of the evolution of consciousness within nature still escape us. What do we know scientifically, for example, about the two major critical points marked by the appearance on earth of the first organisms and the first thought?

Truly it is a distortion of history to see nothing more in it than an enterprise undertaken to recover the portions of truth and beauty abandoned and lost on life's battlefields. These things in themselves could easily disappear without any great loss to us. But what matters supremely to the being that is growing in our consciousnesses is that we firmly gather together the greatest possible number of the threads leading to the modern world and the springs that impelled it, beginning with the vastest and slowest. The past has here and now ceased to be a garden for the curious and a curio-shop for collectors. Its study is only valuable and will only survive as a department of the physics of the universe.

F   *A New Season*

And now, though we have still much to hope from history, how long will this state of things last? Shall we always have something to attract and occupy us in the past? Or will there come a time, as in the case of geographical discovery, when having made a reasonable circuit of the past we shall feel that the moment has come to stop?

In itself, of course, unlike our round earth, the past appears unbounded. Like the wake of a ship, the series of which it is composed arise limitlessly behind the poop of the moving universe. And yet, in this fan whose branches diverge as far as the eye can see behind us, all is not equally useful or accessible to our researches.

In the first place, the part which interests us most (I mean the development of life and more particularly of reflective consciousness) is not really great. Cosmically speaking, man is still quite young. What are a few tens or even a few hundreds of millennia if we wish to study the curve of thought in its shortest harmonics? We could not plunge far in this direction without touching bottom.

Then there arise, of course, in the distance, dark patches which, taken in isolation, might seem accidental, but taken as a whole reveal a sort of absorption of the visibility of objects by time. All historians must have noticed the curious phenomenon by virtue of which the origin of organisms, societies, institutions, languages, and ideas escape us as if the essentially fugitive tracks of these embryonic states were automatically effaced. At very long distances events of great dimensions are in danger of disappearing from our sight also, and in a manner that no instrument can correct.

Finally, even in the most favourable cases, what do we find in the past that is not impoverished, fixed, faded, deprived of everything that made it boundlessly real?

For all these reasons a realm that at first appears to offer no limits to the expansion of consciousness may end by becoming saturated. Once more, do we not receive precisely the impression that I pointed out at the beginning of this essay?

The more I think about these things, therefore, the more I see (without any pessimism but rather with a bound of hope) the possibility of an exhaustion of the past growing before my mind. Of course for a long time still we must examine, one by one, all the remains of history; it is so difficult to be sure whether the very object one neglects may not be the most important. Moreover, the facts which historical research has inscribed for ever in the human memory will continually have to be rethought and reassimilated to suit our new ideas. In this sense the past will continue to be discovered. But for those who come a long time after us these facts whose attainment cost us so much will be accepted on an equal footing with our acceptance of the alphabet or the secret of the stars. The period of the discovery and exploration of the past will be concluded.

At this moment perhaps man will be able to lighten the burden of the museums, collections and libraries without losing any part of his knowledge of the cosmogenesis in which he is engaged. Solidly supported on the axes which have helped him to fix the pattern of history, he will have the right to turn all his efforts to the discovery and utilization of the *living* energies that surround him.

And it will then be the season for a march *entirely forward* which will indeed know no limits.

Then at last man will have understood the essential word whispered to him by the ruins, the fossils and the ashes: 'The only thing worth the trouble of finding is what has never yet existed. The only task worthy of our efforts is to construct the future.'

Études, November 20, 1935. The Red Sea, September 15, 1935.

CHAPTER XIV

THE NATURAL UNITS OF HUMANITY

AN ATTEMPT TO OUTLINE A RACIAL BIOLOGY AND MORALITY

INTRODUCTION. THE AWAKENING OF THE RACES

The nineteenth century apparently ended with a phase of general equilibrium achieved by the mass of humanity. At that moment, 'before the war', the various political and ethnical groups spread over the earth gave the impression of having found durable lines of contact and a definitive interior structure. Over this almost coherent whole, the network of intellectual and economic relationships, fostered by the extraordinary advances of science, was rapidly spreading. And more significant still than this material co-ordination of civilization, an atmosphere of unification and cohesion prevailed in the world. It was the epoch when, in its more progressive sectors, humanity was thinking and speaking internationally.

Now, a few years later, after the shake up of 1914, the situation seems entirely changed. Human blocks that could have been regarded as certainly consolidated tend to fall apart. And this not merely because of the violence of external shocks, but by virtue of a psychic and internal dissociation. The principle and rights of nationalities, brusquely interpreted as the principle and rights of races, not only savagely antagonize neighbours who seemed to be on the verge of understanding, but infect the old national states with the strangest ferments of division. It is as if the human mass, in opposition to the external conditions driving it ever more imperiously in on itself, were reacting by an internal break up.

I will try to throw a little light, drawn from the general history of life, on this unexpected phenomenon which is affecting us so tragically at the present moment. To become aware of it, one has only to observe the loyalties and hatreds it engenders; the present crisis of nations is not a purely artificial movement, nor even strictly rational; and it is by no simple deceit that the masters of the hour seek to justify their excesses by an appeal to the natural demands of certain human groups. At this moment an elementary instinct is at work, perhaps not for the first time, in the depths of humanity. At the root of the racial awakening we find ourselves in the realm of biology.

We must therefore turn to biology – but to a biology adjusted to the dimensions of humanity – if we are to try to understand and direct events.

Origin and significance of races for life in general. Form assumed by the phenomenon of race, in humanity in process of hominization. Probable role of races in humanity.

When we have successfully dealt with these three points we shall be in the position to appreciate, with some appearance of accuracy, the significance of the modern nationalist movement in human history, and finally to draw in broad outline a morality of peoples also.

I. THE RAMIFICATIONS OF LIFE

It seems to me impossible to approach the problem of human races without previously examining a fact to which we are so accustomed that we have ceased to wonder at it: I mean the internal power of expansion and division that characterizes living material. Plants and animals are morphologically distributed in the world around us according to a sort of tree pattern; and ever since Linnaeus natural scientists have spent their lives trying to disentangle its branches. Now clearly this complicated assemblage no more represents a primordial disposition of nature than does the network of watercourses draining a vast river basin. This is no longer in doubt. The tangle of animal and vegetable forms patiently arranged by science in systematic categories is not something born ready made. It has established itself gradually. Life propagates therefore like a morphological fan, each line of which is capable of producing another fan, and so on indefinitely. It ramifies. Let us observe the details of this phenomenon more closely.

When he wants to study the form and propagation of a wave, the physicist first turns his attention to the movements of an isolated molecule taken within the vibrating milieu; and thus he calculates the elementary pulsation or wave, the 'summation' of which will bring him knowledge of the total wave. In the case of expanding life, the elementary phenomenon is represented by the numerical growth of beings at the moment of reproduction. Each living being is capable of giving birth to several other living beings, who at the same time differ from it and differ among themselves. Multiplication and diversification: a double property by which life is defined in its external manifestations. To explain this strictly empirical fact, modern geneticists imagine that the reproductive cells, in the course of their individualizing division, distribute themselves according to the laws of chance, a certain number of characteristics or *genes* defining, by their grouping on the filaments of the cellular nucleus, the 'germ' of the individual to which they belong. Later, by coming together in pairs to fertilize, the cells provided by different individuals put their respective genes into a common fund. Thus each daughter-cell finds its characteristics finally determined by the meeting of genes first contributed haphazard by the two parents, then fortuitously combined by the unpredictable whim of fertilization. One chance followed by another. The number of combinations provided by this machinery being immense, we suppose that the constant increase in numbers of living beings goes hand in hand, as experience shows, with an equally constant change in their appearances. Furthermore the careful study of an animal or plant line over several generations has allowed us to assume that certain so-called mendelian characteristics (colours, for example) are in actual fact distributed among individuals (provided that we take into account the power of genes to become dominant over other genes) according to a predictable law of probability. It has been necessary to point in passing to this 'genetic' theory for it is basic to modern racial science. But I hasten to add that, as we shall soon see, it is far from explaining all the features presented by the tree of life.

Let us now pass over the elementary phenomenon of reproduction in the individual to envisage the case of a whole living group in evolution. From the pulsating molecule let us pass to the wave. What will appear at the final point of this 'integration'? Genealogical trees traced by zoology are most often expressed in linear patterns. This is a weakness which reveals our difficulty in understanding and imagining the play of combinations. In reality each transformation of living forms takes place not in a narrow, linear group but in a multitude, a volume of individuals. The metamorphoses of life have the same form and working in nature as currents in a liquid. They are mass movements within a moving mass. How can we transfer the multiplying and diversifying play of births to the scale of great numbers? If the geneticists were entirely right, that is to say if the appearance of new types obeyed a simple statistical law, we should expect to see the formation of a continuum of variegated types in which all possibilities would be represented according to their degree of probability. Now this is not the result observed in the world of life.

In the first place, far from expanding in a sort of homogeneous network, the totalized mass of individual lines is distributed along a certain number of favoured axes, representing conditions of special viability or stability; as the rain falling in a cloud-burst breaks on the ground into a series of separate streams. Under the influence of ill-determined external or internal causes, the multitude of elementary groups put into circulation by the machinery of each new act of generation, additively forms an ordered and differentiated whole. Thanks to a mysterious sifting of the products of generation, definite groupings or *types* appear: not a nebulous host of individuals but constellations of zoologically classifiable forms.

And this is not all. Certain of the collective types thus appearing (the so-called mendelian species) appear to represent fixed or even reversible constructions. But others (the true species) do not behave like inert aggregates. On the contrary they show themselves to be endowed with some life force of their own, which guides the sum of the individual variations, further produced within them by the play of successive births, in a precise direction. A change initiated in early generations becomes more pronounced in those that follow. Certain fingers shrink; the teeth become more complex; the brain grows larger. Such is the strange phenomenon recorded by science under the name of orthogenesis; and before it the theory of genes, like so many previous mechanistic constructions (natural selection and others) definitely fails. Certain living groups are polarized. Or rather, they 'grow'. Thus the 'phyla' of the palaeontologists tend to take shape – the phylum of the horse, the rhinoceros, the camel – currents of living mass along which a collection of anatomical (or physical) features pass, continually growing, in a single direction. As if the true definition of heredity should be sought less in the transmission of certain characteristics fixed from the beginning, than in the development of some forward impulse.

This is the way in which life's stems are born and grow. Let us simply add to the preceding factors the idea of an angle of divergence between embryonic phyla, and we have all the elements needed to explain the ramifications of living forms in its discernible mechanisms. At the beginning the 'life threads' are only, in some way, virtually separated. Their elements may still meet and fertilize one another, from thread to thread, marginally; these are the races or subspecies recognizable by the subject of systematics. Then the divergence increases, encouraged in many cases by geographical isolation. Lasting interfertilization becomes impossible. Here is the species. Then the morphological separation increases still further. Intercalary groups become extinct, but new threads (races and subspecies of the second order) form and diverge; the species has begun to breed in its turn. Thus we have the genus, then very soon the family, and after that the order, and so on. By the combined play of growth and divergence the bud has become the stem; the stem the branch; and finally the branch has assumed the size of a veritable trunk.

In this general perspective, valid for the whole field of biology, let us fix and remember the three following points on which the rest or my argument depends:

1. Through the very play of reproduction, life maintains itself and advances *by ramifying*.

2. The race forms the first appreciable step in this ramification. It can be considered as a virtual or nascent phylum, not having yet lost the power of crossing with elements of the stem from which it derives.

3. By virtue of the mechanism of ramification by which they are born, morphological groups of all orders that have appeared in nature individualize *pari passu* with their growth. More or less imprecise and confused at the beginning, they become increasingly determined in the course of their isolation. It would be idle therefore to try to describe them at their point of departure. The *purity* of a species or a race (except in the particular case of a mendelian mutation) can therefore only be defined by its success, and in relation to its goal, that is to say by looking forward.

We can now concentrate our attention on the particular case which is the object of this study, that is to say on the problem of races within humanity.

II. THE RAMIFICATIONS OF HUMANITY

A *Existence*

Zoologically speaking, humanity presents an exceptional and strange group. Scarcely separated anatomically from the other primates, strongly differentiated within itself without loss of interfecundity, it behaves in its psychical characteristics as a higher stage, a stage apart in the general edifice of life: as a new world. In one sense, all the features and laws of organic matter are extended and recognizable in man. But in another sense, these various biological properties undergo in him a profound recasting and readjustment. In order to understand him, we must never lose sight of the general conditions of development and functioning valid for pre-human forms. But we must always remember at the same time that these conditions occur in him only in the humanized state.

In view of this, there cannot be any possible doubt that the phenomenon of ramification, so essentially linked to the expansions of animal and plant life, continues to be active in the human mass. And in fact its activity is manifest even to the most common experience. Throughout time men have felt and recognized that they belong to several great families, and that within certain limits these families come together or diverge, and so oppose one another: migrations, alliances, wars. Now to define, more or less roughly, the organic, 'somatic' substratum of these different groups – distinguished from one another in build, complexion, hair, eyes, face – it has become customary to speak of *races*.

In recent times, interested and alarmed by the 'revival of race', anthropologists of all countries have tried to examine with some care the nature of these races of which everyone is speaking. And a good number of them have reached and accepted the paradoxical conclusion that it is impossible to find any scientific criterion allowing the recognition and separation of natural groups within humanity. For geneticists in particular, who are led by logic to define race by the constant and exclusive association of certain genes in the germinal cells, the difficulty has become insurmountable. The discovery in several subjects of a collection of identical genes appearing decidedly improbable, race vanishes: we are confronted only with individuals. Advanced as scientific, this conclusion seems to me to be based rather on a sophism, which bears some analogy to those by which Zeno proved the non-existence of motion. It is correct that, viewed with a microscope, the outlines of human families seem to grow dim. But is this not because a microscope is precisely the most suitable instrument to make them disappear from our sight? On the surface of the water flowing between the banks of a river, secondary currents form, which we can see ramifying and undulating towards us. These eddies are so real that in their fitfulness they sometimes tug dangerously at our boat. Let us try, however, in order to see them, to assume the scale of a drop of water. The currents cease to be perceptible. And even two streams of water taken from the same current may very likely be more different from one another than two streams taken from two different currents. What are we to say? Simply that nothing in the world is perceptible unless one adopts the right standpoint for seeing it. Collective entities or races are only visible at a certain distance. They only appear in large groupings. If you do not sufficiently enlarge humanity you cannot see them properly. Enlarge it too much and they disappear.

To sum up, there *should be* branches in the human species as there are in all other animal species, for since the human group is a living mass it *can only subsist* by spreading along divergent lines. And, in fact, these lines exist, as their multiple interactions, which are at present so unpleasant, superabundantly prove. It would therefore be perfectly idle to deny their reality, but just as idle to attempt a further proof of it. The one thing that matters is to recognize their precise nature, in order to understand their significance, and what we can do about it.

In other words, what form does the power of ramification, which is universally present in living forms, take in the case of humanity in the process of humanization? This is the whole question, and the only one that will occupy us henceforth.

B Nature

The new and specific properties characterizing, either in themselves or in their mutual relationships, the morphological branches continually being formed on the great bough of humanity can, if I am not mistaken, be reduced to two. On the one hand, they are distinguished from all others previously appearing on the tree of life by a recognizable dominance of spiritual over physical qualities (that is to say of the psychic over the somatic). On the other hand, they manifest without sensible diminution an extraordinary power, extending into the far distance, of rejoining and interfertilizing one another.

Let us study these two characteristics in succession.

1. *Predominance of the psychic over the somatic in human groups.* It is still an open question which would merit further study whether the formation of the various zoological phyla that we catalogue might not be much more likely to lead to a psychic dispersion than to an organic differentiation. The very regular appearance, for example, of carnivorous, herbivorous, swimming, burrowing etc., sub-groups might surely correspond at depth with the birth and development of certain inclinations, with certain *internal* tendencies: the evolution of limbs being only the counterpart and expression of the evolution of instincts? Whatever may be the truth of this still rather bold suggestion, no one can deny that in the lower stages of life, each animal line, even if it is not essentially determined by a deflection of a psychic nature, that is to say by the collective evolution of a sort of temperament, at least appears to be doubled and fringed by such a temperament. For reasons of likelihood or convenience systematicians rarely concern themselves with this internal aspect of the species they handle. But natural scientists interested in instincts or behaviour are beginning to make it the object of special study. And they realize that a given form of *Hymenoptera* or bird, for example, can only be fully defined by taking into account not only its external aspect but its method of hunting and making its nest. In certain Arctic rodents, the lemmings, there are said to be two groups almost indistinguishable in their form and coat, one of which is static while the other periodically emigrates south in enormous companies.

Each living ramification, therefore, taken as a whole, contains anatomical and psychic characteristics in close association. It has, in some sense, an outside and an inside, a body and a soul. But this duality is far from being equally pronounced everywhere. In the so-called lower forms, in which the central nervous system is still feebly developed, the psychic seems, at least to our eyes, to be submerged, or drowned, as you might say, by material factors; species and race are principally anatomical. But as, concordantly with the growth and perfection of a brain, spontaneity and the capacity for exchange increase in a living being, the fringe of instincts individualizes and expands round the zoological branch. The soul in the species or race tends to dominate the body. And finally, in the case of the most 'cerebralized' group on earth, humanity, the phenomenon assumes a tangible breadth. In man, whose animal nature is impinged on by thought, the vital ramification should theoretically, and in fact does follow lines that are far more psychic than somatic. And this simple observation already gives us a better insight into an initial and irritating problem.

It has become usual at the present time to contrast race with nation, and nation with civilization, as if they were distinct and heterogeneous entities. If we believe the theoreticians (especially the jurists) the network of cultural unities covering the modern world forms a sort of neo-formation superimposed, without organic links or significance, on the ethnic complex studied by anthropology. Races and nations: two systems discordantly superimposed on unrelated planes.

From the biological point of view, which I am now assuming, this supposed opposition does not exist. On account of crossings to be studied later, ethnologists are no doubt justified in following and distinguishing different zoological lines within a single dominant unity, cultural or national. But this anastomosis is merely an enriching complication; it marks no break in the fundamental phenomenon. Organically and evolutionarily, the two entities are inseparable; they are really one. The *natural unity* into which humanity subdivides is not therefore either the anthropologists' single race, or the sociologists' single nations or cultures: it is a certain amalgam of the two, which, for want of a better term I will henceforth call the *branch of humanity*.

To fix our ideas, let us consider the French. This human family is clearly based on definite ethnical elements, framed and formed by geographical and climatic conditions which are just as definite. But, by all accounts, it also contains, linked to this physical and physiological substratum which it dominates and on which it confers its unity, a group of moral qualities, of intellectual characteristics, of idealogical tendencies, which form a particular spirit and genius. This complex, moreover, is not static. It changes, develops, differentiates, and gradually strengthens in the course of the country's history, in obedience to a law already noted as applying to any zoological branch. It is this ethnico-politico-moral combination that we must consider and take *as a whole and in movement*, if we want to understand *the French branch* without impairing its total biological reality. It is by the continual throwing out of such branches that the power of ramification characteristic of living matter is extended and expressed in the human mass.

Already, in the example chosen, the forces of divergence are in reality not acting alone; they are already complicated by a particular mechanism of coalescence – which, if I am not mistaken, definitely reveals and throws light on the significance and value of race for humanity. But before starting to study this essential phenomenon of synthesis, we must take one further step. We have just recognized the specifically complex nature of the human branches considered in themselves. It remains for us, as has just been said, to observe the no less specific behaviour and characteristics of these same branches acting on one another.

2. *Unlimited mutual fertility of the human branches.* What too closely envelops us automatically ceases to astonish us. To find something in nature to wonder at, there is no need to look at extinct forms. We have only to notice the marvels close at hand in the bat who flits on the membranes of his outstretched hand, in the horse who runs on a single toe, in man, the thinking biped. Is this not enough? A psychological blindness veils our eyes to *the marvels of present phenomena*. This alone explains our indifference to the strange spectacle provided by the zoological structure of the human group.

In pre-human animal forms, as we have seen, the general rule is a more or less rapid isolation of the divergent lines into which the generations divide. Very quickly a break occurs between branches, marked by an incapacity to breed together and causing, on account of the resultant isolation, an accelerated divergence. In this way, as we have said, the race becomes a species, the species a genus, and so on, as the phenomenon propagates.

In man, at least so far as his living representatives are concerned, nothing of this sort happens at the present day; and it becomes progressively clearer that nothing of the kind is likely to occur in the future. Zoological ramification, of course, continues to operate here as in all other living creatures. But one might say that here it leads nowhere, or rather leads *to something else*. Branches are perfectly visible. Somatically, they seem to be at the point which, in an ordinary animal group, would characterize a new species. And yet the separation does not take place on the side of fertility. For, so far as anthropology knows, there is not a single human group on earth, however primitive in appearance, that is not capable of giving birth to limitlessly fertile progeny by cross-breeding with types reputed to be more progressive. A sort of elasticity maintains the cohesion of the fan; and there is no apparent risk of a break. As happens with the leaves of certain trees or the antlers of certain deer, ramification has taken a 'palmate' form. The veins are clearly visible but lying in a limbo in which countless anastomoses remain possible. From the point of view of systematics, humanity presents the remarkable case of a prodigiously widespread animal group in which cross-breeding continues to take place between branches that normally should long ago have become dissociated. For the rest, the phenomenon seems, owing to the exchanges it allows, to coincide with the more and more pronounced establishment of a common psychological atmosphere.

c Complexity

Hence arises the following peculiar situation of the human group considered in respect of its internal ramifications. On the one hand, each of the branches into which it sub-divides consists of *two* distinct elements, the somatic and the psychic, the latter tending to prevail over the former. On the other hand, the different veins formed remain indefinitely capable of reacting on one another, whether by sexual crossing or by the moral and intellectual cross-breeding of their elements. Consequently a vast number of combinations become possible, and in fact take place: combinations in which the psychic and somatic mix and appear in variable proportions, giving birth to units of extremely diverse types.

Here zoologically well separated branches, like the Australians, the Bushmen or the Ainus, probably represent the vestiges of old verticils on the human trunk, the majority of whose shoots have disappeared or become greatly modified.

There great complex masses, the Whites, the Yellows and the Blacks, corresponding, no doubt, to a younger verticil that has now reached its flowering. And then, within these vast unities, broadly coalescing in their zones of contact, other groups stand out, born from complicated mixtures that confuse physical anthropology, but whose psychic criteria allow us to define or suspect all sorts of branches. Sometimes it is the soil factor that predominates, with the idea of a fatherland and the aggressive or pacific characteristics conferred on their respective inhabitants by mountains, steppe, forests or plains. Sometimes it is the political structure in which the nation frames, isolates and forges itself; and this is sometimes capable of reacting in its turn on the racial type, as in the case of the Japanese. Sometimes it is language and culture. And all these various groupings are superimposed and react on one another. They cross, envelop and cut across one another like ripples on the surface of a lake. They form, peter out or establish themselves like eddies arising in a flowing river.

Inevitably the most brilliant mind will finally lose itself in this moving network. But difficulties of analysis should not make us lose sight of the biological significance of the phenomenon or the basic identity of its mechanism. We may be uncertain of the history or the stability of the polymorphous associations which are continually forming, fighting, expanding or disappearing in the human mass. We may, in different cases, give them the most diverse qualifications and values. Nevertheless, fundamentally, they are manifestations of a single life property in action: its power of differentiation in expansion, or I would venture to say its 'ebullition'. Races, countries, nations, states, cultures, linguistic groups; all the superimposed or juxtaposed, concordant or discordant, isolated or anastomosed entities are to the same degree, though on different planes, *natural*; for they represent the direct extensions, in man and on the human scale, of the general process included by biology under the name of evolution.

But then for anyone who admits that the task of science is not solely to reconstruct the past, or to decipher the present, but principally, on the basis of the past and the present, to anticipate the forms of the future, the final question presents itself. If the ramification of humanity, marked by the birth of the various racial or ethnical unities surrounding us, really corresponds to a specific and natural development, what may the range and upper limits of the phenomenon be? Everything has, or at least everything can take a direction in the realm of living things; and nothing in the world seems capable of growing indefinitely without meeting a critical point of transformation. Does the tree structure so recognizable, and in a sense so exaggerated, in humanity simply represent a terminal proliferation of disorderly branches, or may it not correspond, on the contrary, to a *directed movement*, revealed by its very exuberance? Meaningless and purposeless diversifications, or a more or less fertile and convergent harmonization? At what is life working, and towards what are we drawn by human ramification?

Our whole practical attitude towards the problem of race depends on the answer to this question.

III. THE CONFLUENCE OF HUMAN BRANCHES

On reaching this point in my inquiry, I am, as you will understand, leaving the indisputable field of facts to enter, as all sciences have done before me, the dangerous but extremely fascinating realm of hypothesis. *Hypothesis*: a very unsuitable word for the supreme spiritual act by which the dust of experiment takes form and life in the fire of knowledge. A double criterion, of course, guides the advances of thought when it reaches this synthetic phase of its operation. First the general vision which has arrested one begins, without forcing or distortion, to arrange the elements it has called up. And then from the grouping achieved there come a new understanding to the intelligence and new powers of arrangement to the active mind. Coherence and fertility: the two inimitable touchstones, and the two irresistible attractions of truth. Let us interpret the information provided by anthropological and ethnological research, and thus try to provide them both.

For this purpose, it seems to me necessary first to accept the idea, solidly based on sound biology, that the *absolute* direction and value of life are determined by a growth of consciousness in living creatures, which is linked with an increasingly complicated (and consequently increasingly improbable) synthesis of their elements, both taking place together. This rule together with its two close corollaries: (*a*) that man by his faculty of thought represents, in the field of our experience, a point of evolution at present coming to a head; and (*b*) that all further progress of life taking place in man is bound to coincide with a growth of spiritual nature; this rule, I say, appears to be the only guiding thread available to show us the way through the forest of living forms. I cannot enter into a detailed proof of it here. But I cannot advance except by assuming its acceptance.

Having made this statement, I will take as a starting-point, from which I hope to approach the solution I am seeking, a consideration of the following fact. Beyond all doubt, humanity's advance, measured by an increase of power and consciousness, took place in fixed and limited regions of the earth. Historically certain ethnical groups showed themselves more progressive than others, and formed the advancing wing of humanity. Now to what factors do we suppose these groups owed their superiority. Qualities of 'blood' and mind? The best of economic resources and climatic conditions? Yes, no doubt. But we can also see something more. If we look carefully we shall see that the sites of human development always appear to coincide with the points of meeting and anastomosis of several 'nervures'. The most vigorous human branches are by no means those in which some isolation has preserved the purest genes; but those on the contrary in which the richest interfecundation has taken place. Compare only the Pacific and the Mediterranean as they were a century ago.

The most humanized human collectivities always appear in the last resort, to be the product not of segregation but of synthesis. This elementary fact seems to me to provide a solution to the theoretical and practical problem of races. Let us now generalize this observation, that is to say let us extend it to the present and past totality of the human mass. And here a very probable picture presents itself.

In life, as we have seen, at least up to the appearance of man, the rule governing the fate of living branches is divergence. Phyla once born draw apart from one another, and follow their particular destiny at a greater or less distance. After this, they stop and disappear.

The same mechanism operates in man. Divisions start. Phyla take shape. But then everything takes place as if a new influence were coming into play: an influence which not only prevents the branches from falling apart, but also *uses* their diversity to obtain, by *effects of combination*, superior forms of consciousness. Whereas, one might say, that the animal lines dispersed broadly over a field without curves, human lines behave as if compelled to develop on a sphere. Springing from a lower pole (the pole at which they appear), their verticil spreads at first like a cluster of meridian rings mounting towards an equator. But this movement of dispersal, in the course of which forms differentiate, is only the prelude to a reverse movement which will bring together in the upper hemisphere the elements born and consolidated along the course between the poles and make them react on one another in an organically constructed unity. The divergence is preserved, with the perfections it has brought to each branch in isolation; but it is increasingly overcome by a force of convergence which transforms the endless fragmentation in which the unity seemed likely to disappear into a further means of progress. Multiplication develops and completes itself by synthesis.

Thus on the level of man, not only are the individual characteristics of the living being transformed, animal consciousness becoming reflective consciousness; sexuality, love; curiosity, science; inarticulate sounds, language; association, culture. But biological evolution itself begins to change its general mechanism, in the act of hominizing. Not simply the springing up of a certain phylum with greater penetration than all its predecessors. But a synthetic furling back on themselves of the whole further sequence of phyla. A new tactic, one might say, invented by life in order to raise itself to higher states of complexity and consciousness, for the realization of which the old methods were no longer sufficient. Synthesis of groups after synthesis of individuals. A living construction of a type unknown in the past is taking place, all around us, although we are incapable of measuring it.

If this viewpoint is correct, we can expect that, having attained a certain maximum distance from one another, without having ever actually separated, the human branches are beginning to come close together rather than diverge, that is to say are beginning to *coalesce*. To coalesce, I said; not to fuse together, which would be very different. In all realms, organic union differentiates, but does not neutralize the elements it groups together. Applied to the case of races and peoples, this principle allows us to foresee a certain future growth in the uniformity of man's somatic and psychic characteristics; but in combination with a living richness in which the qualities belonging to each of the lines of convergence is recognizably carried to its maximum. The formation of a synthesized human type, on the basis of all the slight variations of humanity that have appeared and matured in the course of history; that, if my hypotheis holds, should be the process at present developing on this earth.

Is this really what is taking place? And if it is, what can and should we do to obey and assist the appeals of a destiny that has become, by thought, conscious of itself at the heart of each one of us?

IV. THE PRESENT SITUATION AND THE MUTUAL DUTY OF RACES

A   Towards Union by Dissension

We pointed at the beginning to the contagious movement which is at present setting the various ethnic unities of the world in bristling hostility to one another. Following a period of humanitarian aspirations, this antagonism between peoples, in which we are caught, seems to give a final lie to whoever dreamed of a unification of the universe. Repulsion, isolation, fragmentation: is not this, as is brutally revealed by the facts, the real cycle of all life, the true human condition?

Observed from the angle from which we looked at things in the last chapter, the event, although losing none of its painful sharpness, assumes quite a different aspect. Believers in the existence of human progress remain scandalized and disconcerted by the revival of racialism. This outbreak of egoistic violence, they think, condemns their dearest hopes. But could one not maintain, on the contrary, that in so far as it satisfies a preliminary condition necessary for their realization, it actually justifies them? Some years ago, it is true, we were able to believe that we had finally reached the platform of synthesis: the point at which the human elements, having more or less reached their goal, had nothing left to do but to abandon themselves to the play of the forces of cohesion. The League of Nations. So, in a mountain walk, as we approach the summit, are we always imagining that we have left the last valley behind? But what, if we are sincere, was the value thirty or forty years ago of the materials with which we flattered ourselves we were building the tower of humanity in its final form? French, English, Spaniards, Italians, Germans, Chinese, all the great branches on earth, had we really reached – are we not still far from reaching – the limits of the power, the genius, the personality that nature is striving to bring out, specifically, from each of our groups? Let us confess that, though we called ourselves 'supernationalists', we were not yet cut to the true measure of a single country. We thought that we were human, and did not suspect (do we really yet know?) what desiring, loving, fearing, suffering meant over the whole area of a single human branch? We are now beginning to feel it in us, and to observe it in our neighbours: before the last disturbances that shook the earth, the peoples scarcely lived other than on the surface; a world of energies was still sleeping in each of them. Well, these powers are, I imagine, still hidden; and at the heart of each natural human unity, in Europe, in Asia, everywhere, they are at this moment moving and trying to reach the light of day: not, I conclude, in order to fight and devour one another, but to rejoin and fertilize one another. Fully conscious nations are needed for a united earth.

Now, at the present moment, we are a prey to the forces of divergence. But let us not despair. In man, as we believe we have recognized, ramification is no longer taking place except in a field of convergence. I do not mean, of course, that we are already undergoing the final preparation in our national existences, after which there will be nothing really left for humanity except to turn inwards and join his ethnic threads together, now that they are definitely formed. In actual reality, a process as vast as that of the synthesis of races is not realized at a single bound, as on the symbolic sphere that I imagined just now. For order to establish itself over human differentiation, it will undoubtedly need a long alternation of expansions and concentrations, separations and comings together. We find ourselves *hic et nunc* in a phase of extreme divergence, the prelude to such a convergence as has never yet been on earth. This is all that I want to say. This, if I am right, is what is happening.

Now that I am on the whole right seems to me to be suggested by the general state of the world, if only we take up a high enough position to see it. At present our attention is absorbed by the retractions and strainings apart of nations. These movements are perceptible on our level and threaten us directly; it is inevitable that we should be over-impressed by them. But the phenomenon is not just a matter of war-threats; it does not seem likely to culminate in separation. The experience of 1914, for instance, with the extraordinary impulse given by war to aviation and wireless, is a proof of this. The arms that each people desperately forges for its defence and separation immediately become the property of all the rest; they are transformed into links that increase human solidarity a little more. It is the same with the sometimes revolutionary industrial inventions, that each country finds itself compelled to make in order to maintain its economic life entirely on its own resources. Lastly, it is the same with the psychological and social readjustments by which each nation thinks it can discover and attain a spiritual supremacy which will make it unique among all the rest. Whatever is progressive and valid in these discoveries or awakenings of consciousness is communicated contagiously and profits the whole human family. In fact, every move we make to isolate ourselves presses us closer together. Power of the mind above, whose convergent curvature inevitably compresses the flux of everything that succeeds in mounting. And power of the earth below, whose limited surface inexorably forces the layers of the human mass in on themselves, the more tightly the more they spread.

So, in spite of the quarrels, which it disturbs and saddens us to see, the idea that a concentration of humanity is taking place in the world and that, far from breaking up, we are increasingly coming together, is not an absurd one. Indeed, without it, I cannot find any explanation that can be applied without contradiction to the phenomenon of man as a whole. The hypothesis that a human concentration is taking place is satisfactory therefore because it is utterly coherent with itself and the facts. But it also possesses the second sign of all truth, that of being endlessly productive. To admit, in fact, that a combination of races and peoples is the event biologically awaited for a new and higher extension of consciousness to take place on earth, is at the same time to define, in its principal lines and internal dynamism, the thing that our action stands most in need of: an international ethic.

B   *The Foundations of a Racial Morality*

As was said long ago, there is no morality without an ideal. How can the peoples of the earth achieve harmony unless they first agree upon the basis of their union? And how can they find the ardour and courage to perform their duty, once perceived, if they do not feel some attraction to it? In the field of collective entities, as in the realm of individuals, whether one likes it or not the Stoic precept, 'Do not do unto others what you would not wish them to do unto you' is no longer adequate. This negative rule may be to prevent the human mechanism from grinding, but it is incapable of starting the motor or driving it forward. It might be good enough to impose peace on a static universe. But, wherever we look in the world, we now see only an uneasy equilibrium. Order can only be established between races and nations by a leap forward. And here is where the advantage of the views we propose shows itself.

One first advantage accruing from our solution, if we accept it, is that there is no longer anything to prevent our recognizing that humanity, taken in its concrete nature, is really composed of different branches. Races exist, but that is no proper reason for the existence of antagonism and a racial problem. In order to escape this problem and save 'human dignity' as a whole, some people feel obliged to deny the manifest differences that separate the ethnical units of the earth. Why should we deny them? Are the children of one family all equally strong or intelligent? Peoples are biologically equal, as 'thought phyla' destined progressively to integrate in some final unity, which will be the only true humanity. But they are not yet equal to the totality of their physical gifts and mind. And is it not just this diversity that gives each one its value? One has this, another has that. Otherwise, why and how should we speak of a synthesis of all? Let us be careful not to repeat, out of ideology or sentimentality, in this matter of races the error of feminism or democracy in its beginnings. Woman is not man; and it is precisely for this reason that man cannot do without woman. A mechanic is not an athlete, or a painter, or a financier; and it is thanks to these diversities that the national organism functions. Similarly a Chinese is not a Frenchman, nor is a Frenchman a Kaffir or a Japanese. And this is most fortunate for the total richness and future of man. These inequalities, which despite the evidence theorists sometimes try to deny, may appear damaging so long as the elements are regarded statically and in isolation. Observed, however, from the point of view of *their essential complementarity*, they become acceptable, honourable and even welcome. Will the eye say that it despises the hand, or red that it prefers not to appear on the same picture with green or blue?

Once this functional diversity of the human branches is admitted, two things immediately follow. The first is that the duty of each of these branches is not to preserve or rediscover some undefinable original purity in the past but to complete itself in *the future*, according to its own qualities and genius. And the second is that in this drive towards collective personalization, aid must be sought from each of the neighbouring branches; an aid all the more carefully applied the more vigorous these have the good fortune to be. As a palaeontologist I cannot harbour any illusions concerning the fact of biological competition or the inexorable forms that it takes. But by the same token I absolutely refuse brutally to translate the mechanical laws of selection into the human field. For if nature clearly teaches us that there is a universal struggle for life, it teaches us no less categorically that, passing from one platform of existence to another, living properties survive only by transformation or transposition. Mutual exploitation and suppression may be the rule among subhuman zoological groups because these are continually supplanting and diverging from one another. In the case of the human bundle, on the other hand, if by our hypothesis it can only progress further by convergence. Brotherly emulation must take the place of hostile competition within it, and war has no more sense except in relation to dangers or conquests outside humanity.

Development of each one in sympathy with all. Graduated organization of spiritual energies in place of the mechanical balance of material forces. Law of teamwork replacing the law of the jungle. We are still far from having performed this delicate but vital transformation on the scale of individuals. Is this a reason why we should not hope that it will finally be realized between nations? Or why we should not at least recognize that outside this ideal there is no biological opening for the future developments of mind on earth?

Of course, it is not everything to have located the peak to be climbed. We have still to climb it. For how long have expeditions been launched in vain at the summits of Everest? Once we have recognized and made up our minds that races and nations must unite, the choice of the route to follow and the question of the methods to be employed still confront us. These are infinitely complex technical problems. How are we to define on the limited surface of the earth, the zones of occupation and the zones of influence, to the best advantage of the whole and of each one? How are we to establish the distinction and hierarchy without which there could only be disorder or fragmentation between unevenly individualized or vigorous human branches? To assure the preservation and progress of its own genius, each natural grouping legitimately requires (these words are inevitably dangerous) a certain space and a certain sorting out of contributions from outside. After all, no organism in the world can maintain itself otherwise. How are we to satisfy this right of each nation to live without infringing the rights of others? How are we to leave the arrangement selected sufficiently pliable to allow of its adjusting, without cracking, to continual new situations? And finally to what extent, throughout these adjustments, can we expect a balance to take place on its own, by the natural play of the forces present, or even rationally to push the resultant in a foreseen direction? Totalitarianism, or liberalism? Hegemony of one group or democracy?

Of course, whatever the circumstances, we cannot answer these manifold questions except by following the method universally applied by life from its beginnings: a slow and patient exploration. But already we know enough (and this is a great deal) to affirm that this exploration will only reach its goal on one condition. That the entire work be conducted under the sign of unity. The very nature of the biological process taking place requires this. Unless they are put forth in an atmosphere of union glimpsed and desired, the most legitimate demands can lead only to catastrophes. We have more than enough evidence of this at the present time. And conversely, in this atmosphere, once created, almost any solution seems as good as another; any effort will succeed, at least as a beginning. Followed from its deepest roots in biology, the problem of races, their appearance, awakening and future, thus leads us to the point of recognizing that the only climate in which man can continue to grow is that of devotion and renunciation in the fraternal sense. Indeed, at the rate that consciousness and its ambitions are increasing, the world will explode if it does not learn to love. The future thinking of the earth is organically bound up with the transformation of the forces of hatred into forces of Christian love.

Now, in virtue of the hypothesis we are following, what is the one power capable of working this transformation? From what source will the branches, and human individuals as well, ultimately draw the desire to accept one another and draw one another towards joyful unity? There is only one conceivable source: a growing attraction to the centre of consciousness in which their fibres and their bundle must complete themselves by reuniting. If we study its most profound features, those of liberty, humanity seems certainly to have reached the stage of its evolution in which it cannot from any viewpoint face the problems presented to it by the growth of its inner energy without defining for itself a centre of love and adoration.

Many of my scientific colleagues will, I know, recoil from this conclusion. But I do not see how they can escape it any more than I can, once they make up their minds to look honestly before them. Just as man (as I have already explained elsewhere) will lose the courage to construct and go on seeking, so he will have no more strength to conquer the inner antipathies which separate him from the joys of unity unless he finally becomes conscious that he is drawing near, together with the universe, not only to some thing but to Someone.

Études, July 5, 1939.

CHAPTER XV

MAN'S PLACE IN THE UNIVERSE: REFLEXIONS ON COMPLEXITY

What is man's place in the universe?

This bitterly debated question is clearly of vital interest to each one of us. It is vital as knowledge: 'What are we?' And vital for our actions: 'What is our value? Where are we going?' And, consequently, 'How should we assess and direct our life?'

You know by hearsay that up to the sixteenth century no one thought of doubting that man was the centre of creation. Man the geometrical centre and the central value of a universe formed of spheres concentrically planned around the earth. It did not seem possible to think otherwise.

And you know also, in this case by direct experience, as a result of a series of discoveries with which we associate the names of Galileo and Darwin, that this rather naïve anthropocentrism of our fathers rapidly melted away in the course of the nineteenth century. Too completely. In the space of a few generations man saw, or at least believed, himself reduced to nothing in a universe in which the living earth had become an insignificant grain of dust in a host of stars; and in which the thinking being now seemed no more than one poor little leaf among tens of thousands on the huge tree of life.

A few more years, and the question might appear definitely settled by science in this humiliating and discouraging sense. Man certainly occupied no very interesting place in nature.

But now the pendulum, having swung to the point of extreme decentralization, shows signs of swinging back towards a more correct middle position. Man no longer the centre of a static world (we have done with that), but man as an element of special, even of principal interest in a world in movement; such is the viewpoint that science is beginning to perceive, by dint of its honest endeavour to transcend itself.

It is to this essentially modern third phase of the discovery of man by man that I wish to introduce you today. But before I make my exposition I should like to offer two important warnings.

1. *First warning.* It is of course understood that in what follows I am expressly, and rightly, taking my stand on the ground of facts, that is to say in the field of the tangible and photographable. Discussing scientific views as a scientist, I must and shall stick strictly to the examination and arrangement of what is perceptible, that is to say of 'phenomena'. Being concerned with the links and order of succession revealed by these phenomena, I shall not deal with their deep causality. Perhaps I shall risk an 'ultra-physical' excursus. But look for no metaphysics here.

2. *Second warning.* The views that I present are still, as I said, only at their birth. Do not therefore take them as universally accepted or definitive. What I am putting before you are suggestions, rather than affirmations. My principal objective is not to convert you to ideas which are still fluid, but to open horizons for you, to make you think.

Three points, as they would have said in the age of Louis XIV, will exhaust the substance of this discourse.

First point. The infinitely great and the infinitely small, 'the disappearance of life'.

Second point. 'The infinitely complex or 'the reappearance of life'.

Third point. 'A universe with three infinites or 'the superiority of man'.

Thus adumbrated, these three propositions must seem to you rather cryptic. Do not be alarmed. Like all great things, what I am going to show you is extremely simple.

A *The Infinitely Great and the Infinitely Small, or the Disappearance
of Life*

To assess the danger that man momentarily ran of finding himself
choked (as a universal value) by the latest advances of science – and
in order to understand also by what expedient he might emerge, more
alive than ever, from this threat of choking – it is necessary, first of
all to consider the dimensions and zones of the universe, as defined by
modern physics.

This perspective can be expressed graphically by the following
table (Fig. 4) in which the principal 'units of matter' so far identified
are arranged in order of linear size (after Max Born, Marcel Boll,
Julian Huxley, etc.)

A simple inspection of this diagram reveals the following details:

1. *Corpuscular structure of the world.* From the base to the top of the
scale, matter presents itself continuously in the form of calibrated
elements, of increasing size, but forming a multiplicity in each case
and at every level. It has been observed that there are electronic
gases, atomic gases and molecular gases. But there are also stellar
gases, and galactic gases. One might also add that there are gases of
living particles; there is a gas of human particles.

2. *Existence of three orders or zones of magnitude within the world.* By a
singular chance, man stands, in the matter of size, approximately at
the centre of the total series (10^2). Below this middle region, the infinitely small (10^{-20}) and above it the infinitely great (10^{25}) (Effect of
perspective? As if our vision stopped at the same distance on each
side).

3. *Vast difference of dimensions between corpuscles belonging to these three
zones.* And here we must not be deceived by these modest 10 cm.
raised to huge powers. 10^6 makes a million. 10^9 a thousand millions,
10^{18} a thousand thousand millions; the 10^{22} cm. of the Milky Way

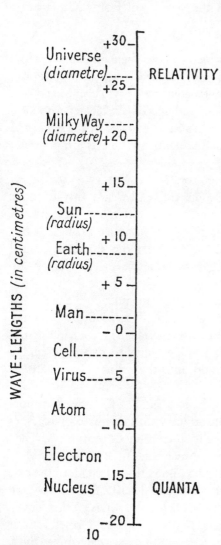

WAVE-LENGTHS *(in centimetres)*

Universe
(diametre)------ RELATIVITY

MilkyWay-----
(diametre)+20

+30
+25
+15
Sun----------
(radius)
+10
Earth-------
(radius)
+5
Man---------
-0
Cell----------
Virus----5
Atom
-10
Electron
-15 QUANTA
Nucleus
-20
10

The universe of two infinities (great and small)
Dimensional scale and properties at either extreme.

signifies therefore a billion billion kilometres, or a hundred thousand light years. Now to descend to the dimensions of the electron, we must follow a path of the same order, in the direction of infinite smallness. Three hundred bacteria, Huxley remarks, could be placed within the point made by our pen in dotting a *i*. Below this, smallnesses become vertiginous. Turned into grains of sand, observed Boll, the molecules contained in a cm.³ of air would form a layer 5 cm. thick over the total surface of France. I may well say vertiginous. Caught between the infinitely great and the infinitely small, man truly floats, as Pascal foresaw, between two abysses.

4. Now (and we come to the third point which Pascal could not even suspect) these two abysses *are opposites*, not only quantitatively, as the extremes of vastness and smallness in the world, but *qualitatively* also in the sense that *the most fundamental properties of the universe become*

different in the very great and the very small from their appearances in the middle zone.

Let us take some examples:

In this good middle zone in which we live, the mass of a body does not vary with its speed; space obeys Euclidean geometry; we can speak unequivocally of the simultaneousness of two events, and plot with no uncertainty the position and speed (simultaneously) of a moving object; light and heat are realities definable by the senses and forming a continuous flux; finally, inanimate objects are generally motionless (continuous phase).

But what happens if we change zone?

On the side of vastness, reason and experience first discover with astonishment, that it becomes more and more difficult, and finally impossible, to speak of simultaneousness. A single clock can no longer measure time for these enormous spaces. Extended to years of light distances, the general time we imagine breaks up into particular times for each system. And, together with this (something still more shocking to our imagination), a new and general curvature seems to appear in space itself. Space becomes spherical. Here two parallels (like two meridians) meet and the sum of the angles of a triangle is no longer equal to two right angles. In this direction we enter, as is said, into the realm of (generalized) relativity.

Let us return towards the infinitely small. Here the metamorphosis of the world is more disturbing still. First the corpuscles, as they diminish in size, are normally in continuous movement. They know no state of rest. And at the dimension of the atom, they seem to be moving at vast speeds (20,000 kilometres a second, in the case of helium ions). It is no longer possible to describe these ultra-small corpuscles in terms of temperature or colour – for it is by their ceaseless movement that impressions of heat and light are formed for our senses. It is no longer possible to attribute to them a determined mass. For at the speeds at which they move the mass will sensibly increase (with the speed). It is no longer possible even to give them (from our point of view, at least) a durable individuality. For, outside their fugitive appearances, they act only collectively, that is to say statistically. Here is what is called the realm of quanta, in which all phenomena break up into an infinity of tiny fragments, all equal to one another, and consequently anonymous and exclusively ruled, for our eyes, by the laws of probability and large numbers.

In fact everything happens as if, at either end of the world, certain properties of matter became exaggerated and dominant, which at the other end of the world were so tenuous as no longer to make a mark on our experience.

Let us provisionally leave on one side (though not forget) this cardinal point of the mutual heterogeneity of the two infinites. It will be useful to us in a moment. And let us confine ourselves for the present to the *abyssal* character of the universe both above and below us.

What is the first effect on our minds of the appearance of these immeasurable depths? Clearly, to make us feel that we are engulfed, annihilated. Squeezed between the vast and the very small, life and humanity seem lost and insignificant. Insignificant in number and volume. What is humanity's thousand million (10^9) compared to the hundreds of milliards of milliards of atoms (10^{80}) that circulate in the universe? And insignificant also in probability. Is it not by an improbable chance that our planetary system was formed by the fortuitous coming together of two stars, and that on one of these planets living organisms should have succeeded in taking shape and maintaining themselves in evolution? So in face of the majesty and ineluctability of the cosmos what remains of our greatness and stability?

'By a hold-up without consequences for the evolution of the universe,' said Eddington, 'some blocks of matter have escaped the purifying protection of sidereal heat or interplanetary cold. Man is a result of this chance fault in antiseptic precautions.'

'To what can life be reduced?' asks Sir James Jeans. 'An apparently accidental fall into a universe which, by all accounts, was not made for it; to remain clinging to a bit of sand, until the cold of death reduces us again to brute matter; to strut for a short hour on a very small stage, knowing full well that all our aspirations are condemned to a final check, and that all we have made will perish with our race, leaving the universe as if we had not existed. The universe is indifferent (or even actively hostile) to every kind of life.'

Vertigo or discouragement.

This inevitably is our first human reaction to the revelation of the two infinites. But is it right and proper that, out of intellectual honesty, we should give in before this shock? Is the priority that the human consciousness has for so long given to spirit over matter entirely false or arbitrary from the scientific point of view? Or in order to preserve spiritual values, are we really reduced to seeking refuge in an impossible dualism as if matter and thought formed two separate universes, mutually co-extensive and yet sharing no common dimension?

It is in order to escape from this paradoxical position, to preserve at the same time the physical value of the spirit in face of matter, and the value of physics in face of spiritual phenomena that I propose today for your consideration a third abyss in the universe, in addition to those of infinite greatness and infinite smallness: that of infinite complexity.

B   *The Infinitely Complex, or The Reappearance of Life*

First of all, what do I mean by the word 'complexity'? By the complexity of a grouping, I do not mean only the number and variety of the elements forming that grouping. I am thinking more of their arrangement. Put together *without order*, the 360 types of atomic nuclei, from hydrogen to uranium, recognized by physics, would form a *heterogeneity* not a *complexity*. As I understand it here, complexity is an *organized*, and consequently *centred heterogeneity*. In this sense a planet is heterogeneous, but not complex. Two different factors or terms are therefore necessary to denote the complexity of a system; one expresses the number of elements or groups of elements contained in the system; the other, much more difficult to represent, expresses the number, variety and closeness of the links (density) existing between these elements at a minimum volume.

Having made this statement, let us return to our scale of cosmic magnitudes (Figure on p. 219) and follow it upwards starting from the very small. Along this line, as we know, the material corpuscles become larger and larger. Now, how do they become larger? Is it, like certain stars, by forming increasingly voluminous aggregations? Not at all (as we now very well know), but by joining together in such a way as to form true 'complexes', in which the atoms group organically into simple molecules, the simple molecules into super-molecules, the super-molecules into micellae, the micellae into free cells, the cells into plants and animals.

Let us now consider these various complexes *as such*, and try, to the best of our ability, to measure their degree of complexity, taking into account, in the first place, only the factor 'number of associated atoms'.

So long as we remain in so-called 'inorganic' chemistry, this number is still small; in the largest molecules it remains about a hundred (10^2) But in organic chemistry, the figures rise rapidly. In the case of the simplest albumins, they reach, or even greatly exceed ten thousand. In the case of the filterable viruses (those enigmatic corpuscles of which one cannot say whether they are still chemical molecules or infra-bacteria), we are already in the order of millions (17×10^6) in the case of the tobacco virus). No one, so far as I know, has yet risked a calculation of the atoms contained in the simplest animal cell. Let us, to be on the modest side, put the figure at rather more than a thousand millions (10^{10}). Since a man is formed of approximately a thousand billion cells (10^{12}), the number of atoms grouped to form our bodies becomes something like 10^{22}. That is to say that we are already in the order of numerical magnitude of the galaxies.

Now, let us note, this astronomical figure expresses only a very small part of what I have called the 'complexity' of a grouping. In a cell, for example, the atoms are not divided in a homogeneous manner (as for example along the radii of a sphere): they form a hierarchized system of corpuscular units of different orders, in which mechanical links are superimposed on osmotic links, which are in their turn superimposed on electronic links (to mention no more than these). In a cm.³ of air, as I was saying, there are three billion billion (3×10^{18}) atoms grouped at random. In a cm.³ of living matter, there are therefore billions of particles in arrangement (one might almost say billions of wheels). The mind is stunned by these facts.

Let us now try to present this complexity symbolically and graphically in terms of size. For this purpose, returning to the vertical scale of the two infinites that we already know, let us place on a horizontal axis the corpuscular complexities as we have just estimated them at a first approximation (that is to say without taking into account the number of links). Then let us fix for each corpuscle the point corresponding at the same time to its dimensions and complication. We thus obtain a curve, which is not far from vertical at the beginning, but is soon almost parallel to the horizontal axis. Let us now interpret this curve. What do we learn from it?[1]

One first thing that appears is that, to represent the universe, not only two but (at least) three infinites must be taken into consideration. A mere reading of the figures shows us that. Complexity, reckoned in the most conservative way, is just as deep an abyss as the infinitely small and the infinitely great. In a universe with only two infinites, higher beings (man, for example) can be considered as 'in the middle'. But in a universe with three infinites, they stand apart from the other non-complex middle-sized magnitudes; they take their place at the summit of a special branch; and in this terminal position (*in which they directly prolong the line of the atoms and molecules*) they form *an extreme*, by the same right as a galaxy or an electron.

They form an extreme, I said.

But now, let us be careful!

At the extremes, as I have already explained, the universe changes form. Its material becomes the seat of new effects. To say that the animals and man represent, along their line, an end of the world, is to state implicitly that, similar in this way to the infinitely great and the infinitely small, they must possess some special property, specific to their particular form of infinite. In the infinitely great, the effects of

[1] Figure on p. 219.

relativity. In the infinitely small, quanta effects. In very great complexes, what?

But why not, precisely, consciousness and freedom?

And this is in fact the perspective that opens. Everyone has known from the beginning that organized matter is endowed with spontaneity in combination with psychic inwardness. Everyone also knows today that this organic matter is amazingly complicated. Why, in the light of the great discoveries of modern physics, should we not state quite simply that two and two make four? In other words, transforming the problem into a solution, why not say this: 'Absolutely inert and totally brute matter does not exist. Every element contains, at least to an infinitesimal degree, some germ of inwardness and spontaneity, that is to say of consciousness. In extremely simple and extremely numerous corpuscles (which only manifest themselves by their statistical effects) this property remains imperceptible to us, *as if it did not exist*. On the other hand its importance grows with its complexity – or, which comes to the same thing, with the degree of 'centration' of the corpuscles on themselves. From an atomic complexity of the order of millions (virus) onwards, it begins to come into our experience. In the higher reaches it shows itself in successive leaps (in a series of psychic 'quanta'[1]). Finally in man, after the critical point of 'reflexion', it takes the form of thought and thereafter becomes dominant. Just as in the infinitely small, great numbers explain the determinism of physical laws; and just as in immensity, the curvature of space explains the forces of gravity, so, in the third infinite, complexity (and the 'centredness' resulting from it) gives rise to the phenomena of freedom'.

Thus everything in the universe around us surely becomes clearer.

And the stars? you will ask. And the galaxies? You have said nothing about them. What place do they have in this story?

Despite their corpuscular appearance, the stars certainly do not form a natural prolongation of the line of atoms. This, as we have just seen, culminates in life in the middle zone of the world. The stars,

[1] These leaps will naturally be related by religious philosophy to the creative pulsations that its principles require.

on the contrary, repeat this line symmetrically on the side of the very great. The stars, one might say, are the laboratories, the place of generation, the 'matrix' of atoms. The larger a star is, the simpler is its constitution. Inversely, the smaller and colder (up to a certain optimum) a sidereal body is, the larger the range of its elements grows, and the more these elements build up into complex edifices. Such is the case of the earth, the only known star on which we can follow the higher phases of this development. From this point of

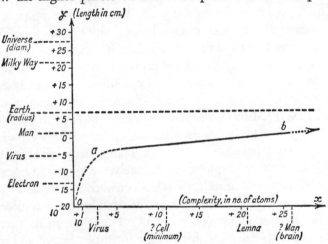

Natural curve of complexities (see text).
a, point of Vitalisation
b, point of Hominisation
The universe of three infinites (Extremely large, extremely small and complex).
Dimensional scale and properties at *three* extremes.

view the appearance of life takes the form of a conjoint effect of 'galactic gas' and 'electronic gas', reacting on one another in the middle dimensions. This, very roughly, is the significance of the higher branch of 'planetization', drawn on the moleculization table above. A clever theory, even an attractive one, you will say. But what is there to prove that this theory is better than others? What tells us that it is *true*?

This is what I have still to prove.

C *The Universe With Three Infinites, in Which Man is Superior*

In science (and elsewhere) the great test of truth is coherence and pro-
ductiveness. For our minds, the more order a theory imposes on our
vision of the world and, at the same time, the more capable it shows
itself of directing and sustaining the forward movement of our
powers of research and construction, the more certain that theory is.
(*True theory* = *the most advantageous.*)

With this understanding, let us take up our position (at least provisionally and hypothetically) in the universe with three infinites
which I have just postulated. Let us act as if this universe were the
true one, and try to see what takes place.

A long series of corollaries immediately appears; and the closely
linked chain of them leads us much further than you would think towards the harmonization of our knowledge and the guiding of our
actions.

In the first place a natural connection is drawn between the two
worlds of physics and psychology, hitherto supposed irreconcilable.
Matter and consciousness are bound together: not in the sense that
consciousness becomes directly measurable, but in the sense that it
becomes organically and physically rooted in the same cosmic process with which physics is concerned.

In the second place, and by the same fact, the appearance of consciousness ceases to be a chance, strange, aberrant, fortuitous occur-
rence in the universe. It becomes on the contrary a regular and
general phenomenon connected with the global drift of cosmic matter towards increasingly high molecular groupings. Life appears
wherever it becomes possible in the universe.

In the third place, the phenomenon 'consciousness' by the very
fact that it is recognized to be general, tends to present itself as essential and fundamental. Not only *a* physical phenomenon, but *the*
phenomenon. We have already known for some years that towards
the bottom matter tends to vanish by disaggregation of atomic
nuclei. And here is life, showing itself as symmetrically the exactly
opposite process: a corpuscular aggregation. On the one hand, a fall

of great numbers towards states of greatest probability. On the other a persistent, incredible but undeniable rise towards the smallest numbers by way of improbability. The movements are of the same universal vastness. But while the former destroys, the latter constructs. Must it not then be this latter rise of consciousness that represents the true course of our universe through time: the very axis of cosmogenesis?

And hence (fourth corollary) the significance of man is growing, and his place is becoming scientifically more precise.

On the curve of moleculization, as we have just drawn it, man is clearly not the first in size. By the quantity of corpuscles assembled in his body (by his total number of molecules) he clearly stands below the elephant or the whale. But on the other hand, it is certainly in him, in the thousands of millions of cells of his brain, that matter has now reached its maximum of linked complication and centralized organization. Chronologically and structurally, man is indubitably, in the field of our experience, the last formed, the most highly complex and at the same time the most deeply centred of all the 'molecules'.

There are still certain physicists who scoff at 'man's pretensions to give himself an inexplicable superiority in the world'. I am certain that, a generation hence, the attitude accepted by scientists will be that of Julian Huxley when he declared that man is the highest, the richest, the most significant object within range of our investigations, because it is in him that cosmic evolution is culminating at this moment before our eyes, having become, by our reflexion, conscious of itself.

The old anthropocentrism was wrong in imagining man to be the geometrical and necessary constitutional centre of a static universe. But its anticipations are verified in a manner at once higher and more humble, now that man (who was once believed to be engulfed in a universe immensely extended by physics) justifiably reappears at the very forefront of the wave of moleculization which carries the world forward.

Everything falls into place, everything takes shape, from the lowest to the highest, in the present and the past of a universe in which a generalized physics succeeds in embracing without confusing the phenomena of radiation and the spiritual phenomenon. *Coherence*.

And, in addition, everything is illumined (though in a diffuse manner, as is right) in the direction of the future. *Fertility*.

I wish to insist on this decisive point before concluding.

One evident characteristic of the curve of molecularization, as drawn, is that it is not closed, not stopped. At present it ends with man. But dare we think that it can and should extend further? And how? Man is momentarily a *climax* in the universe; and a leading shoot also, to the extent that by his intense psychism he confirms the reality and fixes the direction of a rise of consciousness through things. But may he not also be the *bud* from which something more complicated and more centred than man himself should emerge? Here there appears a possibility, of which I cannot develop the proofs and details here, but for which it is essential to mark a place in a general perspective of a universe of three infinites, such as I am presenting.

In man, up to now we have only considered the individual edifice: the body with its thousand billion cells, and above all the brain, with its thousand millions of nervous nuclei. But while man is an individual centred in himself (that is to say a 'person') does he not at the same time stand as an *element* in relation to some new and higher synthesis? We know atoms as sums of nuclei and electrons; molecules as sums of atoms; cells as collections of molecules. Could there not be, in formation ahead of us, humanity as the sum of organized persons. And is not this, moreover, the only logical manner of extending, *by recurrence* (in the direction of greater centred complexity and greater consciousness), the curve of universal molecularization?

Here is the idea, long dreamt of by sociology, reappearing today, this time with a scientific foundation, in the books of professional scientists (Haldane, Huxley, Sherrington and so many others). Fantastic, you may think. But must not everything be fantastic, if it is not to be false, in the direction of the three infinites?

Here, of course, there are no absurd fictions.

Impossible still to form an idea of the modes or appearances that might be adopted by this formidable hyper-cell, this brain of brains, this Noosphere woven by all intelligences at once on the surface of the earth. All that we can say of it is that, in this absolutely new (and therefore unimaginable) type of bio-synthesis individual liberties can only be imagined as carried to their maximum by the very play of their mutual association. But if any attempt to imagine the *form* of the human future would be idle, and even dangerous, it is already a great deal to be able to foresee the *dimensions* and *existence* of this future. We are now beginning to understand what we shall have to do during the billion centuries of life that according to the astronomers still await humanity. And henceforth we can define, according to our knowledge of the extent and density of the cosmos, the general line of advance that we should try to follow: by way of ever more conquests towards ever greater unity.

Now, once launched in this direction, it will be impossible for us to stop. And this is why.

When, climbing the curve of complexities, one reaches the highest realms of consciousness, there is not only an awakening of new properties. A particular form of energy appears also or, to be more exact, a sort of new curve manifests itself, in which all the other forms of energy are furled. It is not enough, in fact, that man has at his disposal the requisite power to synthesize beyond himself. He must also *have the will* to do so. And for that he must have the *taste* for going further; that is to say, under the influence of a sort of internal gravitation, he must be *drawn* upwards, from within. Humanity, devoid of this taste, humanity not drawn towards 'more being', would infallibly and rapidly become extinct; even astronomical piles of calories placed in his hands would not save him.

Now what is necessary, if we are to agree not only joyfully but passionately to push on the increasingly heavy and complicated work that cosmic synthesis requires of us? What conditions must the universe absolutely fulfil in order that we may be drawn towards ever greater consciousness?

This (according to all those who have tried to discover the psychological mechanism of action) is the condition: that we shall not imagine the movement that beckons us forward to be condemned in advance to stop or draw back. We must know that it is, by nature, *irreversible*. Promise man as many millions of years as you will. Let him glimpse at the end of that period as high (that is to say as super-human) a summit as you will. If it is known beforehand that, once that summit is reached, we shall have to descend without any signs of our ascent surviving in the universe; then, I say plainly, we shall not have the heart to advance, and we shall not advance. Whatever Jeans and Langevin may say, man will never consent to labour like a Sisyphus.

In order to balance our conceptions of the universe it is not enough, therefore, to arrest the 'curve of moleculization' at the formation even of a planetary consciousness. It is, moreover, impossible to suppose that, like the lines of space, it will curve backwards by way of refraction. By virtue of the new conditions imposed on it by the appearance and demands of reflective thought, capable of criticizing its future and refusing to progress, men must agree that its trajectory will definitely leap forward in the direction of a supreme place of personalizing centration and consolidation. It is from this place of irreversibility, in fact, once discovered, that the light breaks backwards, illuminating the secret mechanism of the phenomenon. At first, we could only note with astonishment, but not explain the persistent rise of a fraction of the world, against the current, towards ever more improbable states of complexity. Now we understand that this paradoxical movement is sustained by a prime mover ahead. The branch climbs, not supported by its base but suspended from the future. That is what renders the movement not only irreversible but irresistible. From this point of view (which is that not only of simple antecedences, but of causality itself) evolution assumes its true figure for our mind and our heart. It is certainly not 'creative', as science for a brief moment believed; but it is the expression of creation, for our experience, in time and space.

And it is thus, in the end, that above the rediscovered greatness of man, above the revealed greatness of humanity, not violating but preserving the integrity of science, the face of God reappears in our modern universe.

My purpose in writing these lines was, I remind you, to open new horizons for you, to make you think.

Well here is the thought I leave you to reflect on:

Once the partition separating the conscious from the inanimate is broken for science by the admission of the great complexes into our thought, an energetics of the spirit becomes superimposed on the energetics of matter. The balance of the world is no longer entirely expressed by Einstein's formulae (which are in fact only valid for a universe with two infinites). But in a world with three infinites we must, to save the *whole* phenomenon, introduce terms and values of action. *Since it has become human*, the world cannot continue to advance towards greater complexity and consciousness except by making an ever more explicit place for the forces of expectation and hope, that is to say for religion.

And since there are many Christians among my audience, let me add this for them:

Towards the end of the nineteenth century, the Christian view of the world might have seemed to certain eyes limited and out-of-date because at the base of its theories it maintained intransigently:

1. Faith in a God, personal centre of the universe.

2. Faith in the primacy of man in nature.

3. Faith in a certain totalization of all men in the bosom of a single spiritual organism.

Is it not remarkable that by precisely these three characteristics which seemed to mark it out as a decayed and out-of-date doctrine, but which we have just rediscovered, all three (at least in the form of indications) in our universe of three infinites, Christianity now tends to present itself to reason as the most progressive religion?

And now, in conclusion, one more observation.

One of the consequences, as I have just said, of the theory of the three infinites is to make us sense, for the future, the establishment on earth of a more highly organized and centred form of humanity. Does not the terrifying spectacle of the present war give an empirical contradiction to this prophecy, and therefore to the whole system that advances it?

I think not.

The pain and scandal of the times is, in my opinion that, submerged like miscroscopic elements in the transformation taking place, we suffer it in detail and from within. Its elementary shocks overtop and mask from us the general progress of the phenomenon. The trees conceal the forest.

But let us imagine an observer standing on a star who has found the means of following by a sort of spectral analysis the gradual development around the earth of a sort of halo of thinking energy, which I have ventured to call the Noosphere. There is no doubt that for such an observer our planet, having continually gained psychic energy for the last 500 million years, must at this moment be coming to an explosion, which it has never experienced before, of ever increasing consciousness. For never, most certainly, at any moment of the three hundred thousand years of their history, have human atoms been more numerous, or more closely involved with one another, or brought to such a pitch of psychic tension *in their totality*. Compressed in a murderous body – tension still charged with hatred, alas! But for the distant observer whom we have imagined, these inner frictions and rendings might appear secondary. What he would observe, what he would record in his scientific reports, would be a step forward, a critical step in the foreseen direction of higher states of consciousness and higher unity on the earth's surface.

Let me end with this optimistic affirmation, based not only on feeling but on an examination of the most fundamental movements of the universe:

'Examined in the light of a general world science capable of giving spiritual energies their place in a third infinite, the crisis we are passing through bears the 'positive sign'. Its characteristics are not those of a break-up but of a birth. Let us not be frightened therefore of what at first sight might look like a final and universal discord. What we are suffering is only the price, the annunciation, the preliminary phase of our unanimity.'

Unpublished lecture given at Peking, November 15, 1942.

CHAPTER XVI

ZOOLOGICAL EVOLUTION AND INVENTION

Around us humanity proffers the curious spectacle of a vast animal group in the course of arrangement (both physical and psychic) which is increasingly driven in on itself. How are we to interpret this phenomenon of socialization? Does it simply represent an accidental and secondary regrouping in nature, without precise bioligical value or significance? Or, on the contrary, must we see in it the natural and legitimate extension (on a higher plane and more finely ordered) of the same movement that has always drawn living matter towards states of increasing complexity and consciousness? This, as is too often forgotten, is a vital question for the moralist and the sociologist preoccupied with rationally determining the directions and laws of human destiny. But, as I wish to point out here, it is a fundamental question also for the biologist working on the problem of the transformations of life. Let us try, then, to assume the second hypothesis: the one in which the social phenonomenon displays an arrangement of truly evolutionary and organic value. From this view-point (the plausible aspects of which I have tried, following so many others, to bring out in another place), it is clear that a very particular method of scientific investigation is placed in our hands.

If in fact the zoological process of evolution is actually being pursued in human collectivization (and, one must add, in the self-transformations to which man will soon be genetically and morphogenetically capable of submitting his own organism; that is to say, if man is (as Julian Huxley has written) only evolution which has become 'reflexively' conscious of itself: then it logically follows that by way of introspection we should be in the position to understand directly, in the very modalities of our action, at least certain of the factors that formerly presided over the transformations of life. And one idea particularly seizes our mind, that an important role in the appearance of new zoological characteristics might perhaps be ascribed to the 'forces of invention'. This means that we cannot *completely* explain the appearance and placing of the wing, for example, or of the fin, or even of the eye and the brain without *some reference* to the psychic faculties and procedures introduced by the builders of the innumerable machines with which we are every day extending our powers of locomotion, action and vision. In order to know how life operates (if it is really life that operates in us), is it not enough to watch ourselves at work?

Of course two fundamental difficulties appear immediately as theoretical restraints on the practical use of this method of reasoning. On the one hand, even if it is admitted that from *man* (a reflective animal) *onwards* the 'invention' factor becomes dominant in the advance of evolution, nothing proves *a priori* that *below man*, the action of this factor is not so weak as to escape all observation. On the other hand, and in addition, even admitting that in these pre-human animal forms the psychic element appreciably controls the morphological, nothing guarantees that this psychic element (of non-reflective type) may not be so different from ours in its conditions and functioning that all comparison remains illusory and sterile.

Nevertheless the problem is presented – and inevitably so – by the case of man: we have to know whether a place should not be left open for the effects of consciousness in the mechanism of zoological evolution. We should rightfully remember this each time a residuum appears in the analysis of this evolution, which is irreducible to the ordinary factors of chance, heredity and selection. Indeed, is it not a gamble (not to say a contradiction) to try and explain the constant drift of organic matter towards always more improbable forms of arrangement by a simple play of probabilities? Life, undoubtedly, sets up automatisms that we must understand scientifically. But does it set them up purely *automatically*? That is the whole question.

Today, beneath our eyes, 'invention' is a factor in an undeniable human orthogenesis. When, and under what forms, did this régime begin? And at what depths in the layers of life?

Contribution to international conference held in Paris, under the auspices of the Centre Nationale de la Recherche Scientifique, April 1947.
Paléontologie et Transformisme, Albin Michel, 1950.

CHAPTER XVII

THE VISION OF THE PAST

WHAT IT BRINGS TO AND TAKES AWAY FROM SCIENCE

In the direction of the very great and the very small, by means of super-giant telescopes and the electronic miscroscope respectively, modern science tries with all its might to develop a power of vision into space, on which scientifically everything else depends. Less noticed, because slower and less publicized, but just as intense and persistent, is its parallel effort to increase our perception of time along the only path open to such researches: in the direction of the past. Only yesterday, the physicist and chemist might have viewed the ant-like labours of the legion of excavators (geologists, palaeontologists, archaeologists) all bending at different levels over the archives of the earth, with a detached or even amused curiosity. Today the hidden meaning of their investigations (often more instinctive than deliberate, it must be confessed, in the investigators) begins to appear, After great efforts of calculation and much technical finesse, the great mirror of the Palomar telescope was cast and erected last year, and this will double the stellar depths accessible to our eyes. At the same time, if we look for a final direction and purpose in the accumulated labours of all those engaged in the rediscovery of the past, will it not quite simply be the preparation of a layer of time thick enough for characteristics and properties to appear (thanks to this same thickness) which would remain invisible or unnoticed in a thin durational layer? At present, by a pooling of the stratigraphic and radio-active methods developed in the course of a century's work, we have a layer of between six hundred and a thousand million years at our disposal. At this degree of enlargement, what modifications take place in the structure and colours of the earth around us?

I will point to two in particular, whose complementary effects seem to me to govern with increasing strictness our perception of past time in all realms: the first is *the appearance of slow movements* and the second *the automatic suppression of the first terms of every series*.

Let us study, one after the other, these two effects – the first clarifying, the second distorting (or at least 'accentuating') – exercised on our picture of the phenomenon by a much enlarged vision of the past.

A *Appearance of Slow Movements*

Despite the fluidity and brevity of our individual existences, the universe has appeared to human eyes for long ages as an immense realm in equilibrium – the very movements of the planets, apparently so perfectly regulated, being only a particular form of this fundamental stability. Examined in a thin layer, the base or background of our individual movements seems to be formed of a vast and homogeneous immobility (sidereal, telluric and biological) – as if a certain number of rapid changes (our lives) were drawn and ran on the surface of some immovable platform. The ancient cosmos.

Now as our methods of penetrating and reconstructing vanished eras become perfect, it is precisely this platform or residuum, apparently unchangeable to our eyes, that begins to move: not as a single whole but as if gradually breaking up into a system of waves of increasing length (astronomical, orogenical, climatic and biological), each increase of thickness in the sheet of the past prepared by history revealing to us a slower rhythm of greater breadth. Once upon a time everything seemed fixed and solid. Now everything in the universe has begun to slide under our feet: mountains, continents, life and even matter itself. If we look at it from a sufficient height, we no longer see the world revolving, but a new world gradually changing colour, shape and even consciousness. No longer the cosmos, but cosmogenesis.

One of the greatest surprises that man has received in the course of his exploration of nature has been the discovery that the lower he descends towards the very small, the closer he comes to zones of extreme agitation. At sufficiently great degrees of enlargement, that is to say on the colloidal scale and below it, all inertia resolves itself into movements of incredible rapidity. Now an analogous phenomenon takes shape before his eyes, no longer under the miscroscope, but thanks to the complex modern machine so patiently constructed to thicken time. By the simple deepening of our perception of the past, the stuff of the cosmos begins to vibrate at all levels down to its lowest depths; not this time by way of irregular jerks, but along a rich variety of well-defined curves, among which two particularly interesting pairs of movements stand out, demanding a moment of our attention: movements of orthogenesis and diversification: movements of pulsation and drifts.

1. *Orthogenesis and diversification.* Of course the observation of a 'layer of the past' at any level can yield to us only the traces of movements, not the movements'themselves. Not living trajectories therefore; not continuous lines; but a sequence of *serially* distributed states; something like a design *pricked out in points.* An investigator of the past must therefore examine and study everything throughout the centuries which presents itself to his gaze in the form of a *discontinuous series.* Now, empirically, two very different types of groupings stand out among the collections thus discovered and isolated. Very often (as is proved notably by geological superimposition of different levels) the terms of the series studied are disposed *successively* in time. Then one can be certain that the dotted line defined by an observer really belongs to a linear genetic process: birth and development of a range of mountains or a zoological type. But at other times, it happens, on the contrary, that a scale of states or forms submitted to a stratigraphic test shows itself to consist of terms which are not spaced in time but approximately simultaneous (the case, for example of the 'fan' mutations which occur at the earliest beginnings of the great zoological groups). And in such a case it becomes clear that the series under consideration does not belong to a trajectory but to an 'explosive wave' of forms: the effect not of gradual growth but of

almost instantaneous diversification. The attention of historians of the world and of life was for a long time engrossed by the first type of developments (evolutions of the 'orthogenetic' type). But now it is increasingly roused and attracted by these evolutionary phenomena of the second kind (evolutions of 'dispersive' type) to which both the series of stars (red, blue; dwarf, giant, etc.) and that of simple bodies (having long been regarded as more probably of orthogenetic structure) now finally seem to owe their origins: not phyla but *spectra* of stars and atoms.

2. *Pulsations and drifts.* Important though the dispersive effects, whose duty, one might say, was to support the world's expansive and exploratory power by the play of diversity, show themselves to have been in the past, it is always, in the final analysis, to the differential progression of the different parts of the universe along certain favoured axes (that is to say to orthogeneses) that we must return in order to try and understand what 'evolution', as we call it for want of a better word, means and where it is leading us. Now here too an objective examination of the facts observed at a great distance introduces an important distinction into the central idea – which is not so simple as might at first sight appear – of directed linear transformation. As a result of the essential mechanism by which, as we have said, slow movements in the past only become distinguishable to our eyes in succession and in their increased order of magnitude, it was natural that researchers' eyes should first have perceived evolutions whose period was relatively short. Hence in geology so many systems based on an oscillating mechanism either of marine encroachments or geo-synclinal folds. Hence, in palaeontology so many reconstructions principally concerned with disengaging the successive replacements of one fauna by another. Hence, finally, in human history, the preference shown by Spengler or Toynbee for the recurrent play of types of civilization. Now, however, underlying those very pulsations, waves of ever-increasing length are coming into view. And these waves are so flat and so slow that we can no longer say, from our marginal position, whether they too are of a periodic

nature, or on the other hand show singular and irreversible drifts. Such, underlying astronomical cycles of all orders, is the presumed expansion of the universe; such, throughout the superficial diversity of geological ages, is the uninterrupted emergence and hardening of the continental masses; such, beneath the flux and reflux of the great zoological groupings composing the biosphere, is the irresistible complexification and cephalization of nervous systems. To bring to our perception, far beneath all surface waves, these deep-down tides must surely be the supreme aim and reward of our efforts to dive as deep as we can into the abysses of the past.

B   *The Suppression of Origins*

Though these traces of 'directed movements' reveal themselves clearly and irrefutably and occur in increasing numbers, in the distribution of beings and events observed in a growing thickness of time, one difficulty or anomaly remains, against which every attempt to establish a coherent interpretation of the past has for long hurled itself. About the certainly objective reality of very numerous trajectories left by life in the course of development no doubt is any longer permissible to anyone. But how are we to explain it then that precisely these trajectories, if we try to trace them to their origins, refuse to connect with one another, and remain as if hanging in the air? If everything is born, in a universe in genesis, how is it that we cannot find any true beginning of anything?

The curious structural antinomy of a past which, on the one hand, unyieldingly imposes itself on our experience as having originally formed a sub-continuous current, and which yet, no less patently, breaks up under our eyes into a heap of frozen and disjointed planes, has for long seemed, to many good minds, decisively opposed to any idea of a common evolution of living and inanimate matter.

Now it is quite evident at present to any biologist or historian with a modicum of up-to-date information that the alleged contradiction, so often quoted in argument, between fluidity and stability in the current of life is only a simple optical illusion, arising from the intrinsic characteristics of all 'beginnings' in the world of phenomena. Any birth (whether individual or collective), is naturally a very short event; and it results in all cases in the appearance of frail organisms which are then subjected to a rapid development. Whether in the case of ontogenesis or phylogenesis, the embryo and the newly-born are beings with a maximum of morphological variability and, at the same time, with the minimum resistance to destructive actions from within and without. Under these conditions, is it not absolutely inevitable that, in a space of time large enough to allow the development of an animal or vegetable phylum to take place, the first phases of that phylum (that is to say precisely the most connective and the most malleable) automatically disappear from the field of our experience (since they have not affected for sufficient time a sufficiently large group of individuals strongly consolidated in their structure)? By the simple selective wearing down of time, the true primitive stream of things tends naturally to reduce itself to a series of stabilized *maxima*. With age, the traces of evolution become frozen and 'atomized', in such a way that everything seems to arise ready-made before our eyes. This is the simple answer to many of the difficulties that we strike in our attempts to reconstruct the past.

In the case of the oldest branches of the tree of life, this explanation might be hailed unkindly as a convenient stratagem invented by transformists who find themselves cornered. But in this case, and within a zoological group as certainly evolutionary in type as humanity, the same law reappears. Must it not be playing exactly the same role? That is to say, are we not just as incapable of perceiving the origin of the first Greeks or the first Chinese as that of the didelphians or the amphibians? Better still, and as I have often said: In the case of indubitable beginnings of which we have been direct witnesses (cars, aeroplanes, etc) is it not certain that if our metallic contraptions could fossilize, the palaeontologists of the future would never suspect (unless they were to unearth a museum), or never recover the rudimentary types which preceded the manufacture of our most highly perfected, most standardized and therefore most widely distributed models.

Inevitably and invariably, the vision of temporal distance, while isolating and bringing out one after another the great rhythms of the universe at the same time blots out the original traces and characteristics of their birth. Just as erosion, by attacking a fault in the terrain, gradually hollows out a valley where at first there was only an imperceptible fissure, so the work of centuries ceaselessly amplifies for our eyes any natural impulse of growth in any realm of things. To thicken the past is not only to shake it optically, therefore, and set it in movement; it is also to reduce it to thin layers, to 'hyperquantify' it. In palaeontology of course (to take only this particularly simple case) thanks to the continual discovery of sometimes sensational 'intermediate types' researchers are persistently and almost unceasingly[1] adding to the steps between the present and the earth's most distant horizons. They now rise one behind the other as far as the eye can see between the present and earth's farthest horizons. No capricious distortion of the landscape, of course; since the voids created by the 'time factor' in the historical series becoming wider when we are dealing with the slower and more ancient movements, the general relief of the map is corrected and accentuated by each added step. But there are still lacunae. In time and space the distinguishing power of our most perfect instruments cannot exceed a certain limit, beyond which our knowledge will always see a gaping zone of indeterminacy.

Therefore (a paradoxical fact) the study of the mechanism of origins must resort in the final instance not to the past but to the present. A delicate and deceptive pursuit since many things (and precisely the most revolutionary, the most inward, the most far-reaching) generally begin around us, beneath our eyes, without our being conscious – except too late and after the event – of what is taking place. But a pursuit facilitated in two ways: by the ever-increased detail and certainty with which everything that happens on the face of the earth is recorded in our various archives; and also (but this would demand a special study) by the fact that it is probably not in the

[1] See P. de Saint-Seine, 'Les Fossiles au rendez-vous du Calcul' (Fossils mathematically cousidered). *Études*, November 1949.

faraway past, at the beginnings of the universe, that these things happened, but ahead, in the direction of the future in formation. It is here that those events which are truly characteristic of species and societies are being prepared, within the vision of the natural scientist and physicist. Here are the great beginnings.

Contribution to the international congress on the Philosophy of the Sciences held in Paris from November 17 to 22, 1949.

Études, December 1949.

CHAPTER XVIII

EVOLUTION OF THE IDEA OF EVOLUTION

In the course of recent years the idea of evolution has greatly evolved, so much so that one notices with amazement how many criticisms even now addressed to biologists by the 'profane' are completely wide of the mark.

I will reduce the points which have been affected by this 'evolution of the evolutionary idea' to three. Since the heroic times of Lamarck and Darwin one may say that the notion of zoological evolution has been (1) clarified, (2) universalized and (3) centred on man and 'hominization'.

Let us examine these points briefly in succession.

1. In the last century, to begin with, the idea of evolution has *clarified*. At the beginning, the notion of transformism, as it was called, was still impregnated with metaphysics (if not with theology too). Since that time, it has been presented scientifically only as an authentic phenomenology, entirely attached to the study of a *process* (chain of antecedences and consequences); there has been no intrusion into the realm of 'natures' and 'causes'.

One still reads in recent works: 'Evolution, a theory to be condemned since it affirms that the greater springs from the less.' It is time they stopped bothering us with this argument. In so far as it is possible to define in the natural movement of evolution an absolute direction for man, all that modern evolutionary theory declares is that in the spatio-temporal reality of the cosmos the great *succeeds* the less. And this is both indisputable, and un-condemnable.

A *process* is not a philosophical *explanation*.

In our empirical universe, everything *is born*, everything establishes itself and *grows* by successive phases. Everything, including the

All. This is essentially what we see today, and apparently for ever, in the world around us.

2. Now, thus understood and clarified, the idea of evolution (this is my second point) has not ceased to *universalize* in the course of its progress. Appearing locally, in the wake of zoology, evolution, after making gradual progress through the neighbouring realms, has finally *invaded everything*. In conservative circles the natural scientists are still held responsible for this perverse theory. But now, increasingly, all nuclear physics, all astral physics, all chemistry are in their manner 'evolutionary'. And the whole history of civilization and ideas is at least as much so.

Let us be done once and for all, therefore, with the naïve conception of the 'evolutionary hypothesis'; it has long been out-of-date. No, taken sufficiently broadly, evolution is no longer, and has not been for a long time, a hypothesis – nor merely a simple method. It is in fact a new and common dimension of the universe, and consequently affects the totality of elements and relations of the universe. Not a hypothesis, therefore, but a condition which all hypotheses must henceforth fulfil. The expression for our minds of the world's passage from the state of 'cosmos' to the state of 'cosmogenesis'.

3. And now finally, having reached this stage of universalization, the idea of evolution is tending (if I am not mistaken) to make one further decisive step, being now led by a convergent multitude of facts to *find its axis* and to concentrate on *man and hominization*.

Let us thoroughly understand this.

Initially, that is to say a century ago, man considered himself first of all as a simple observer; then after Darwin as a simple branch of evolution. But now, as a result of this incorporation in biogenesis, he is beginning to perceive that the principal shoot of the tree of earthly life passes through him. Life does not diversify by chance, in all directions. It shows an absolute direction of progress towards the values of growing consciousness; and on this principal axis man is the most advanced term that we know.

It might seem that after Galileo man lost his privileged position in the universe. Under the increasing influence of the combined forces of invention and socialization, he is now in process of recapturing his leadership. No longer stable but in movement; no longer standing at the centre but acting as the leading shoot of the world in growth. Neo-anthropocentrism, no longer of position, but of direction in evolution.

Bulletin de l'Union Catholique des Scientifiques Français, June–July 1950 (Contribution on Religious thought in relation to the fact of evolution).

[Editor: We have thought it interesting to compare with this discussion three authoritative opinions on evolution, expressed at later dates:

'It is scarcely necessary to say that the only natural arrangement which can be applied in zoology and botany is based on phylogenesis. And this leads us to modify completely the presentation hitherto used in textbooks. Instead of vertical lists with connecting brackets, we must use the image of a branching bush as an image of the evolutionary movement'. Lucien Cuénot L'Évolution biologique, Paris, Masson, 1951.

'In short, in so far as any event that no one has witnessed and that cannot be reproduced can be held as a fact, evolution may be so held. To deny evolution, we should have to admit that a malicious Creator had cleverly 'rigged' his creation in order to impose the idea of transformism on the human mind.' Jean Rostand: Les grands courants de la Biologie, Paris, Gallimard, 1951.

'The principle of evolution is nothing but the scientific method itself applied to all realities of all nature developing in time. It is the only means at our disposal of trying to discover the law of their expansion and order of succession, whatever their ontological substratum. Without it, one could only build up a descriptive catalogue of things, but could not attempt to understand them.' Abbé Henri Breuil: Bulletin de Littérature Ecclésiastique published by the Institut Catholique de Toulouse in collaboration with the Centre National de la Recherche Scientifique, January 5 1956.]

CHAPTER XIX

NOTE ON THE PRESENT REALITY AND
EVOLUTIONARY SIGNIFICANCE OF A
HUMAN ORTHOGENESIS

We have often had occasion to write, and with good reason, that the development of empirical research was increasingly revealing itself all around us – as an effort to discover smaller and smaller units in nature. But could we not say with equal reason that parallel with this continual advance in the direction of the very smallest bodies, what characterizes and animates the development of modern science, is the search for very vast structural movements affecting the world in its major natural divisions, or even in its plenitude, in the whole of its material?

It is from this point of view, in any case, that certain phenomena, in appearance particular or local, are periodically made to assume a dominant importance in our intellectual constructions, owing to the fact that, in a narrow but extremely sensitive zone, they allow us to. perceive a new universal drift of things.

Such, in astrophysics, is the reddening of the light of distant galaxies, which (perhaps) betrays a headlong expansion of the sidereal into space.

Such, in biology, are the (less noticed) effects of ultra-socialization and ultra-reflexion, by which a fundamental and still active tendency of matter to arrange itself ever more closely and ever more consciously on itself is beginning to make itself decidedly felt in the case of man. This is the point that I wish to make most insistently in these pages.

But in order to understand this correctly, let us first of all define some biological terms (or to be more exact some functions), which are too often confused in discussions on the subject of evolution.

A *Preliminary Definition: Speciation, Phyletization and Orthogenesis*

1. *Speciation.* For modern biology, as we know, a species has lost all metaphysical significance; it no longer represents anything but a mutually fertile collection of individuals whose morphological variations are grouped statistically around a mean type (corresponding to the maximum ordinate of a simple Gauss curve).

In this perspective the phenomenon of speciation (or formation of species) represents the secondary appearance (by mutation) somewhere within a population thus composed of one or more statistical centres at which morphological grouping takes place: the curve representing the frequencies consequently presenting *several maxima,* susceptible under the influence of factors which are still obscure (geographical isolation, for example) of separating from one another biologically, as if the initial species had given birth, by fission, to one or several new species.

At first sight, simply a phenomenon of *dispersion*; and resulting, in appearance at least, in the establishment, in each case, of a *stabilized* population.

2. *Phyletization.* Observed in their numerical distribution *at a given moment,* the individuals composing a single species group themselves, as we have just said, around a median type, representative of the species. Let us now consider, *over a sufficiently long time,* the sum of all the species issuing, by successive fissions, from a determined (or a natural group of) species. Are these various daughter-species distributed purely by chance, equally *in all directions* around the mother-species? Experience clearly and universally answers, No. But, by the effect of large numbers, they in their turn tend to group themselves within a certain 'field of fire': the type *Equus,* the type *Felis,* etc. Here too, that is to say, no longer on the individual scale but on that of the species, a statistical maximum takes shape. Observed in a sufficient number of cases and over a sufficient interval of time, repeated

THE VISION OF THE PAST

speciations give birth throughout the ages to general alignments: the effect, we say, of *phyletization* – or, which comes to the same thing, of *orthogenesis*; this latter word meaning simply in this context the appearance in time within related species, of a statistically oriented distribution.[1]

Taken at a certain degree of generalization, orthogenesis (so harshly discussed by biologists) is, as can be seen, a perfectly simple and obvious notion. For it merely expresses the indisputably 'fibrous' and 'radiating' aspects that everyone can see in the texture of the biosphere.[2]

Where the real difficulty and the true interest begin is when, taking a further step forward, one comes to ask:

1. first, whether (and in what proportions) the *indisputably directed* additive quality of 'speciating' mutations in certain privileged directions (phyla) is seated:

(*a*) in a particular structure of the external milieu within which the successive mutations operate: passive orthogenesis or *ortho-selection*.

(*b*) or, on the contrary, in an internal (conscious or unconscious) 'preference' of the living being to follow one direction rather than another: active orthogenesis or *ortho-election*.

(2). And then (second question, less often put, but perhaps more critical still) whether under the generic term 'orthogenesis' or 'phyletization', two processes of unequal importance and depth (although biologically related) have not been fortuitously confused:

(*a*) the first of *speciation*, leading to the birth of increasingly divergent and *differentiated* forms.

(*b*) and the other of *complexification* (or complexity), this latter

---

[1] Actually (elementary) orthogenesis has *already* been responsible for the morphological grouping in a Gauss curve of the individuals composing each species. But it is only in phyletization that by the magnifying action of time, the phenomenon stands out in all clarity.

[2] No one would think of maintaining today that zoological phyla are in no way 'genetic', that is to say that they correspond to a simple intellectual arrangement of a sufficiently great number of elements fortuitously diversified in all directions; as grains of sand or the pebbles on a beach might be grouped in series, in order of size or shape.

producing, along *all the azimuths* of specialization (with more or less success but in every case) zoological types increasingly centred and cerebralized. Armed with these different notions (which are at the same time questions), let us return to the subject of the phenomenon of man.

B   *Persistence and Acceleration in Present Day Humanity of an Ortho-
genesis of Complexity*

Studied in its zoological roots and its fossil stem, the human group forms an element (or more exactly the *head*) of a phylum. This fact is no longer open to question; indeed it never seriously has been. Whether we derive them directly from the anthropoids, or prefer to regard them as a sister branch, the hominians take their place, historically and morphologically, in either case, at the end of a long series of speciations (or, one may perhaps say, of a vast population of species) statistically forming a trail from the Eocene to the Pliocene: the drift taking place along a principal and median axis of growing 'anthropization' (rounding of the cranium, flattening of the face, development of hands, increase of height, etc.) At the very heart of the sub-family, taken at its beginnings (lower Quaternary) a movement of orthogenesis is already well marked, leading (some fifty thousand years ago) to the emergence of the *sapiens* type within a very complicated bundle of pre- (or para-) hominians.

On the question of man's evolution in the past, I repeat, all biologists and palaeontologists are fundamentally agreed, beneath the diversity of the terms they employ. Opinions begin to diverge, on the other hand, or even passionately to differ, when the moment comes to decide precisely whether, at the stage of differentiation that he has now reached, *Homo sapiens* is or is not still malleable and undergoing some organic movement of ultra-hominization.

In the opinion of a good number of scientists (and not the least important: K. W. Gregory, Vandel, etc.) this question should be answered in the negative. For, after all, say the representatives of this first school, is it not evident that, anatomically speaking, man has reached a dead end, from which (leaving out of account some slight progress still to be expected in the direction of an increasing brachycephalism and a further flattening of the face) it is impossible for him to emerge?

Man has come to a *dead end*.

May I remark once more how ill such a perspective (however much it is favoured by those who for all sorts of reasons do not want to see the world around them, and still less man, in process of movement) agrees with the extraordinary vitality of an animal group, which appears by all its characteristics to be, on the contrary, in the full flight of expansion and organization? Never on earth before has such a quantity of living matter reached so high a state of fermentation. How then can they convince us that it is here, in this (human) mass precisely, raised to boiling-point that the forces of speciation have been suddenly extinguished? This is absurd.

In order to get a really clear view of the present situation of planetary life, the moment has come, if I am not mistaken, to introduce the distinction between the two orthogeneses of specialization and complication which I have already outlined.

The osteological differentiation of man may well have reached its limits. But that the essential vital process of complexity-consciousness has reached its ceiling in him, that is quite another matter. Indeed there are two major reasons why we should seriously doubt it.

On the one hand, even if we do not leave the plane of individual anatomy, there is nothing to prove absolutely that important evolutionary assets (a more developed arrangement of the nerve fibres) may not still be held in reserve in our brain substance.

And on the other hand, if (ceasing under the pressure of facts to confine the realm of biology to *cellular* groupings) we decide on the better course of regarding the psychogenic[1] arrangements of individuals in social systems as properly 'organic and natural', then instead of the famous dead end of which so much is spoken, surely we must interpret the *present-day* structure and deportment of the human

[1] By the expression 'psychogenic arrangements' I mean increases of complexity accompanied by increase of consciousness.

group in a very different way, as an extraordinary evolutionary leap. An entire phylum (no less!) all of whose fibres (the old as well as the new-born) instead of being isolated as a result of divergent speciation, converge and rapidly furl in on themselves, as I have so often written, under pressure, at once geometrical and psychic, as a result of thought reflecting on itself in a confined space.

Faced with such an upheaval, how can we doubt the reality and nature of events? A higher form of cerebration, no less – not elementary this time, but collective – in which not only the subordinate and secondary nature of the orthogenesis of specialization compared with that of complexity[1] is fully discovered; in which not only the continuation around us of an organic folding in of the world on itself, but also, by virtue of this intensification and enlargement, the mechanism and springs of evolution are fully revealed.

C *Human Orthogenesis and the Forces of Evolution*

Just now (in the paragraph of definitions) I indicated in passing the *a priori* alternative with which the biologist is faced, when confronted with the indubitable reality of a phyletization of living matter.

Where can he look, I asked, for the explanation and seat of the phenomenon? Should it be (as the Neo-Darwinists believe) in the automatic and blind action of some external regulator or 'filter'? Or, on the other hand, (as the Neo-Lamarckians maintain), should it not be rather in the play of some *internal* factor of arrangement, capable of seizing and adding up a certain favoured category of chances as they occur?

It is a remarkable thing that *once* the existence of a 'human orthogenesis of speciation' is *recognized*, it brings a decisive answer to this apparently speculative question, which has more importance than we often think for the conduct of our lives. For if, on the one side, it is at last scientifically admitted that the technico-psychic organization of

[1] In fact one might say that in man (and it is perhaps here that his evolutionary individuality lies) there is a coincidence between orthogenesis of speciation and orthogenesis of complexity, on a single common axis of 'cerebration.'

the human group represents an authentic extension of zoological evolution; and if, on the other, it is undeniable that this organization, taken in its most active and sensitive part (I mean the realm of *re-flective* research and invention) is an operation *planned from within*, then we must certainly yield to the evidence. However preponderant in our experience the role of the external forces of chance in the phyletization of the initial and lower forms of life, from man on-wards, *at least*, the influence of certain internal forces of preference unmasks itself, emerges, and tends to come into the forefront of biogenesis.

In other words, to repeat an expression employed a few pages back, since man and in man (to the extent that he ultra-hominizes himself by collective cerebration) the mechanism of *ortho-selection* tends increasingly to give place to the effects of *ortho-election* in the expansion and accentuation of the life-phenomenon on the surface of the earth.

Since man and in man, simple evolution tends gradually to mutate into auto- (or self-) evolution.

With the following practical consequence:

From a thermo-dynamic viewpoint, I do not feel myself equipped to discuss the nature and laws of what one might call the *specific energy of arrangement* in nature. Perhaps cybernetics will help us to do so.

What is the numerical difference between the energies of two systems formed of the same objects more or less well arranged artificially? In other words in what and why does the effort exerted by the invention and perfection of a watch or an aeroplane differ from the simple material labour of manufacturing and assembling the various mechanisms of these objects?

I will not try to pin-point it here. But in a *régime of auto-evolution*, this 'arranging' form of energy (energy of invention and combina-tion) appears and (despite its incredible smallness in terms of 'ergs' or 'calories'), begins to play an increasingly decisive role in the progress of the world. This is quite certain, and sufficient to confront the en-gineers of tomorrow with a whole series of unexpected problems, relating both to the optimum growth and utilization and the nourishment and preservation of the psychic forces of evolution.

How – for everything finally returns to this – can we preserve and intensify the *self-evolving mechanism* in man, not only the *power* but, at a still deeper level, the very *taste* for arranging and 'super-arranging' the stuff of the world in and around him?

This, I presume, even more than questions of war and peace, is the fundamental problem fated to become in the future the principal preoccupation of humanity. Within the universe which organo-physically is gradually collecting on itself as a result of complexity/consciousness, what faith or what attraction will help us to assure the completion of an orthogenesis of centration ('ortho-centration'), the progress of which directly leads to the increased independence of the 'auto-centric' aspects?

A whole new and generalized energetics in which, following the axis of growing corpuscular arrangements, a dynamic contact is established, without producing confusion, between the forces of matter and spirit.

Unpublished, Paris, May 5, 1951.

CHAPTER XX

HOMINIZATION AND SPECIATION

THE PRESENT DISCOMFORTS OF ANTHROPOLOGY

INTRODUCTION

Despite the growing number of its practitioners, anthropology has great difficulties in becoming a true science. And for this reason: that, contrary to the essential method of science, it continues to approach man *frontally*, as a unique and isolated object (if not *per descensum* even, starting from philosophical or sentimental principles), instead of attacking him, as it should, *per ascensum*, mounting towards him from the 'corpuscular' along the natural and genetic path of what we now call 'evolution'.

At present the science of man is vegetating because it is still no more than a branch of humanism equipped with technical terms. But on the other hand, in order to escape the humanists it requires only one perfectly possible condition: the final establishment of a relationship of an energizing nature prevailing all along the line, between physics and the human phenomenon.

I have already[1] suggested on several occasions that such a relationship is furnished by the visible process of complexity/consciousness which, 'at right angles' to entropy, irresistibly by the play of great numbers, draws a fraction of matter simultaneously to arrange and interiorize itself on itself; human socialization being, from this point of view[2], merely the highest phase of the 'complexification' and

[1] See, for example 'The Phyletic Structure of the Human Group', *The Appearance of Man*, p. 132; and 'La Réflexion de l'Énergie' (The Reflexion of Energy), *Revue des Questions Scientifiques*, October 1952.

[2] As proved by its *psychogenic* effects (planetary intensification of reflexion within humanity).

'growth into consciousness' of the biosphere. Resuming this same idea from a slightly different angle, I should like to insist here on the absolutely *natural* manner in which (whatever far too many anthropologists have against it!) the singular terrestrial event of hominization, taken in the anatomical and cultural totality of its characteristics, organically extends the biological phenomena of speciation into the *thinking* realm. This observation has two results: firstly, it clarifies our ideas concerning either the most fundamental and general or, on the contrary, the most singular qualities of the zoological group to which we belong; and secondly, it rouses our sense of species in regard to this group in a new form.

A   *Animal Speciation. General Characteristics of the Process and its Function*

Physicists have discovered that to the innumerable particles in motion which constitute the atom, the 'wave' function is inevitably joined.

Similarly, biologists are beginning to understand, that the function 'species' must necessarily be associated with a multitude of individuals forming the same living group.

On the one hand isolated living particles do not (and cannot) exist in the universe. There are only populations.

And, on the other hand, a population is empirically inconceivable outside a stream of *speciation*.

Let us spend no time here on the first of these two propositions (it is outside my subject) by which in fact the essential corpuscularity of the stuff of the universe is merely extended (first at the cellular, then at the metazoic level). And let us concentrate our attention on what I have just called 'speciation'.

Speciation. In what exactly does this particular biological function consist? Ill-defined only a few years ago, it is now in process of presenting itself (by way of a more persistent analysis of the functions of micro- and macro-evolution) as a fundamental and universal property of organic matter.

At a rough approximation to *speciate oneself* (or more simply and directly to *speciate*) is, for a portion of living matter, to break up statistically into a certain number of pieces, each defined by a certain collection of common characteristics. The most elementary scientific textbooks are already full of these bell-shaped curves in which, within a genetically connected population, one sees individuals grouping themselves numerically around a median type (summit of the bell), like shots around a bull's-eye. At this first stage of simple quantitative distribution, one might perhaps say that the species is not only statistical but static; in fact, though the curve representing the group may seem to adjust itself or even slightly to oscillate under a continuous increase of observations, it remains, by and large, unmoved and self-conforming.

Now, empirically the process shows itself to be much more complicated and subject to movement than one might think.

On the one hand, by virtue of the phenomena called *mutations* (*modification of the genes in the chromosomes*) it happens periodically[1] that the curve of the species becomes double, thus giving birth,[2] by the appearance of a new peak, to a new species. And on the other hand, followed for a sufficiently long time (palaeontological eras) the successive series of daughter-species thus engendered manifests the remarkable property of following the line of growth-in-value of a group of definite characteristics, the successive mutations not dispersing by chance, but reinforcing one another *by addition*.[3]

In short:

[1] For obscure reasons which are certainly connected with the play of the reproduction and multiplication of individuals within each statistical mass.

[2] At least potentially, the cleavage being completed only if the conditions of survival prove favourable to the mutants.

[3] I will not attempt the question whether, in addition to this 'orthogenesis' by accumulation of successive mutations, there may not be reason to consider another more profound additivity, marked by the continuous accentuation of certain characteristics (reinforcement of genes) within the species itself. Let us remark, at all events that, related to this notion of *additivity* (quite outside any idea of 'finality') orthogenesis is an essential and primary attribute of speciation.

Persistent aggregation of biologically neighbouring individuals into mutually fertile populations.

Periodic and progressive segmentation of these aggregates, as an effect of chromosomic changes.

Cumulative intensification, in time, of certain characteristics along this chain of successively individualized aggregates.

The better and further we know it, the less conceivable, by very virtue of its corpuscular nature, living matter seems divorced from these determinants of a certain 'speciating' operation, the astonishing characteristic of which is (however much the terms may seem to contradict one another!) to raise atomic matter *irresistibly* in the direction of ever-higher, that is to say always *less probable* arrangements.[1]

Of cosmic necessity, every scrap of life is subject to speciation, and the *more living the more subject*. Man is therefore less likely than any living creature to escape it.

B   *Speciation in Man. Persistence of the Fundamental Mechanism and Singularities*

One still sometimes hears it said (and by specialists in human questions) that humanity is only a word or concept, to which nothing in nature precisely corresponds.

We must however make up our minds that since the coming of biology and genetics, such a proposition (still possible in the time of argument over universals) has no more meaning in the modern world.

Considered in his true nature, man can no longer be treated in any way as an abstract entity; nor can a cut be arbitrarily made in the continuum of animal forms. Just like the cats and the dogs, he represents at the very least a statistically grouped mass of related and

---

[1] The reconciliation of the two ideas of determinism and indeterminacy included in the process will no doubt be discovered to be an effect of great numbers combined with an 'innate' (and therefore scientifically inexplicable) preference of the stuff of the universe for higher states of complexity and consciousness.

approximately similar individuals. *At the very least*, I repeat, man is a species like the rest. And that alone would suffice to 'confound' all those who still try to approach the study of the phenomenon of man from the direction of nominalism or conceptualism.

But we can say more, apparently. And it is at this precise point that the problem presented by evolution to modern anthropology appears in all its breadth.

Not only, to repeat my phrase, is man a species *like* the rest, but furthermore and above all, he is *more* of a species than the rest:

(*a*) First, because he represents a species which has *biologically broken through* (into the reflective).

(*b*) Then, because in him, as a consequence of this emergence, speciation operates at a new stage (the 'cultural');

(*c*) And finally, because within this new compartment or realm opened to life, the species tends to pass from the aggregate state to the form of centred unity (phenomena of acculturation and convergence).

Let us study one after another these three successive steps in a human ultra-speciation, 'steps' still bitterly disputed (or systematically ignored) today, though inevitably agreement will be reached after a short while, under the combined pressure of empirical evidences and our urgent need to act.

1. *The break-through into the reflective.* Far more numerous than the nominalists or conceptualists just mentioned (and far more harmful to the development of a true science of man) are the 'confusionists' who, abusing the word *intelligence* (or perhaps simply not understanding it completely), go about repeating[1] that a simple difference of *degree* (and not *of nature*) separates the human psychism from that of the anthropomorphs; and that for the rest, in more general terms, it is out of anthropomorphic illusion that we judge our 'mammalian' form of knowledge to be qualitatively superior to that of the insects, or even perhaps of the bacteria.

[1] Following the great Darwin himself, alas, in the *The Descent of Man* (quoted by Leslie A. White, *The Science of Culture*, p. 22).

A specific difference, or no specific difference between humanity and the simple living creature.

On this fundamental point (on which the future of anthropology at present depends), it seems to me here and now possible – if not necessary – to take up the following scientific position:

On the one hand – as we all know by direct inner experience – man is an animal psychologically endowed with the property not only of knowing but *of knowing that he knows*.

On the other – the fact stares us in the face – man, *because he is reflective*, shows himself (he and *he alone* among living creatures) capable of weaving an autonomous biological network of planetary dimensions.[1]

In the present state and language of science this situation seems to me[2] simply inexplicable unless it is admitted that:

(*a*) In life (as in the case of every other variable dimension in the world) there are a certain number of successive possible boundaries.

(*b*) Towards the end of the Tertiary, as a result of some neuro-psychical transformation,[3] man (the *first* and *only one* of the animals[4]) crossed one of these boundaries. This leap, in its fashion, has profoundly modified and renewed the face of the earth as the emergence of the first living proteins had done, a thousand million years before.

In man, let us recognize once and for all, evolution, the self-same evolution is continuing, but past a critical point of speciation which causes the new species to change its biological stage – and conduct.

2. *Speciation and culture.* Man, because reflective (and therefore

---

[1] What I have come to call the 'noosphere' (above the biosphere).

[2] To me, and fortunately to many others with me. See, for example, Leslie A. White *The Science of Culture* (N. Y. Farrar and Strauss, 1949). For White the specific quality of humanity is to be sought in the power of 'symbolizing': the direct (but in my opinion only secondary) effect of reflexion.

[3] An event whose existence is certain, though it is not yet definable in its mechanism.

[4] 'The first and only one'; for if any other living form had had the chance before it, that form would have woven the noosphere, and man would never have appeared on earth.

planetary) inaugurates a new form of life: a life of the second degree, or a life of the second order, if you prefer.

It is because of an inaccurate assessment of this renewal that the 'isolationist' atmosphere has arisen in which, as I said at the beginning, anthropology is still languishing. Humanity: not merely another living species but another world, a little closed and self-sufficient world, playing the great game with its special rules and, more particularly, definitely escaping from the repressive laws of speciation. Let us pick up any book of anthropology. In nine out of ten, only *Homo sapiens* is discussed. And, in ten out of ten, it is stated or understood that, for twenty thousand years at least, *Homo sapiens* has represented zoologically a sort of invariant, over which the forces or waves of what they call 'socialization' flow only superficially, that lack any biological roots. Well, this is the place to affirm that there is certainly some fault of vision, somehow hidden, in modern anthropologists, which it is necessary to correct.

Humanity has lasted for many thousands of years. Not only has it lasted but unceasingly strengthened and intensified itself, at an accelerating pace, before our eyes. So how can we avoid concluding that, by virtue of one of the most certain and universal laws governing cosmic material, it must continue, in one way or another, to complexify both organically and statistically, since, as we recalled above, for a living group to propagate and to ramify are exactly the same thing? *A priori*, by the sole fact that he survives (and even 'super-vives') we can be sure that man, following some still ill-identified process, is in course of 'speciating' more intensely than ever, at this very moment, beneath our eyes.

And where, whatever may be said, but under the form of culture, in the realm of his socialization?

For some years the idea of *culture* has gradually become isolated, and has finally impressed itself with strange urgency on the minds of ethnologists. 'Culture', that is to say a technico-economico-mental complex, free and individual in its constituent elements and at its beginnings, but rapidly becoming supra-individual and more or less autonomous in its developments. Patently, the anthropologists are puzzled and defeated by what seems to be the 'individual life' of these local agglomerations of procedures, customs and ideas which, once they appear, last, increase, and attract or repel one another, like physical *vortices* or living organisms. They describe them; but definitely, as they see and theorize about it, the phenomenon remains 'in the air'.

Under these conditions, therefore – and since *we know* for certain that there is a speciating quality somewhere in man, why not, once and for all, recognize and agree, despite the determined resistance of the 'leaders' (nearly all non-biologists) in the sciences of man, that *natural evolution and cultural evolution are one* – to the extent that the latter represents the direct extension and accentuation of the general phenomenon of organic evolution in the hominized world? In man, as the psychological effect of reflexion, the technico-mental becomes additive (cumulative) to a degree never reached even by the insects. And at the same time, speciation invades the psychic realm and rebounds into a new space.[1]

And by the same token our problem is resolved.

Cultural differentiation = hominized speciation.

Far from being verbal and confusing, as its enemies suggest, this equality (or identity) undoubtedly brings a coherent and fertile simplicity to our perspectives. On the one hand, rather like the famous equations of Lorenz and Einstein in physics, it defines the evolutionary unity of the universe from the biological point of view.

Then, by the fundamental analogies that it suggests and proves, it opens the way to new researches in the thinking layer of earth.

Lastly (and one might say principally also) it provides us (as we shall see) with the awaited explanation and the necessary courage to confront the extraordinary phenomenon of human totalization, arising before our eyes.

---

[1] This extension of speciation into the cultural does not of course rule out (but this is another story) a possible (natural or even 'artificial') recurrence in humanity of chromosomic mutations. Under present conditions cultural development does not seem to modify the genes, its specific heredity being apparently not of a chromosomic but of an 'educational' nature.

3. *Man: a convergent species.* As I have already mentioned cursorily, the various cultural unities that have appeared in the course of human history possess not only a remarkable power of self-growth, but also react continually on one another, following a process to which anthropologists have given the name of *acculturation*, though without appearing to suspect either the extent or the general direction of the phenomenon they are considering.

For specialists in ethnology, acculturation reduces itself in practice to the effects of mutual contact between two Indian tribes, or perhaps between a native population and a centre of European penetration. These effects are, moreover, studied only locally, and most frequently only from the point of view of the weaker ethnical element, that is to say the more easily 'metamorphized'.

Now, by all the evidence it is quite another thing (and a very different thing!) that has been going on throughout the centuries in the melting-pot of human civilization.

On the one hand, by gradual stages (and at a speed that has increased with the acceleration of exchanges) the effects of acculturation have unceasingly *knitted themselves together* till they now form a planetary network.

And, on the other hand, within this *continuum* certain dominant groups have appeared, unceasingly also, among whom the process of acculturation is moving towards a *higher order of magnitude* – leading at each stage to a numerical reduction and an intensification in the power of the cultural centres in sight.

Let us consider this extraordinary process of concentration (which presents anthropology with a problem that it does not seem yet to suspect) and let us bring to it the equation just expressed and accepted:

Culturation = speciation:

Here again one (and only one) interpretation of events seems possible: a paradoxical interpretation, I admit. But in science must not truth be extraordinary in order to be true? And this is to admit that in man, as a result of the 'agglutinating property' of addition in a reflective milieu, speciation (without ceasing of course, to send out continuous new shoots) no longer proceeds in a divergent, but a *convergent* way.

Man is not only, statistically and genetically speaking, a good species. He is also something more than a zoological species that has escaped into a new realm.

But, more specifically still, he represents the only case in the field of our experience of a species which (because at once reflective by nature and planetary in extension – the one because of the other) tends irresistibly[1] to knit itself together materially and psychologically until it forms in the strict biological sense a single super-organism of a definite nature.

A remarkable extension and confirmation indeed, for our intellects, of the law of complexity-consciousness.

But also, let us observe in conclusion, a precious comfort arriving just at the critical moment, for certain moral distresses within our hearts.

c   *The Reawakening of a Sense of Species in Humanity*

As an effect of hominization, that is to say by penetrating the realm of reflexion, the zoological group to which we belong is undergoing a profound transformation in its texture. Among the animals surrounding us, the individual is apparently not well separated from those preceding or following it, and from those all around it: innate co-consciousness and primacy of reproduction, as if the individual were less alive than the species. In man, on the contrary, as a result of the rapid accentuation of psychic autonomy in each thinking element the phylum tends in some manner, and at a first view, to 'granulate' and even to break up; as if the individual tended to live in isolation and for himself. And consequently, we really seem to have reached a point where very little of that sense of species that we can speculatively define *in its animal form* is still left in us. This endangers our internal equilibrium in two serious ways:

(*a*) First, because it leaves us floating, disorientated, or even divided (because pulled apart) each within ourselves.

[1] On account of the very force and irreversibility of speciation.

(*b*) Secondly, as a result of the fact that nothing, at first sight, seems to give any sense to the 'absurd' cultural maelstrom in which we are caught; the most obvious effect of which seems up to now to have been to disintegrate and mechanize us rather than to bring us to ultra-hominization.

Charybdis of a life that is aimless because dispersed: Scylla of a collective and depersonalized existence.

It seems more and more evident that only one thing is capable of bringing us victoriously past these twin perils. The sole event to be hoped for at the point of hominization that we have reached is the appearance in the world of a psychic flux (impulse, passion, faith, etc.) powerful enough to *reconsolidate in freedom*, both with themselves (on the individual scale) and with one another (on the planetary scale) the emancipated multitude of human molecules.

And it is here that the dynamic value (one might say the value of salvation) of an awakening of our minds to the enormous phenomenon of human convergence comes into sight.

For after all if, for solid scientific reasons, we were finally to admit (fully, once and for all) that far from repelling one another by nature, the thinking corpuscles are cosmically polarised towards the sort of arrangement in which each of them is fated to find, as a result of *collective reflexion*, its own true goal, then this totalization that so alarms us would automatically mutate from the materializing and enslaving form in which we see it at present into an attractive '*unanimity*'; it would become *transfigured*.

To actuate simultaneously, the one by means of the other, the spiritual unity at the heart of each man and (which may seem to us improbable)[1] the spiritual unity between all men together, nothing more (and nothing less) would be necessary than the still awaited establishment of a field of sympathy on the planetary scale. Now just such a field is provided by a *renewed sense of species*, which will make each individual conscious of forming, not only a link in a chain, but an integrable element in a system in the course of personalizing unification.

[1] Although they are at bottom one and the same thing.

This, however, requires one condition (which I will not develop here for fear of being wrongly accused of indulging in metaphysics); which is that, for the convergent species of a new type to which we belong, the supreme point of speciation to which we are tending must at the same time be a point of penetration:[1] not an end, the anticipation of which would kill the taste for 'super-vival' in us, but a new beginning in a quite new realm.

A theorem of pure energetics, if properly considered; in which the study of the genesis of living forms, pushed to its conclusion unexpectedly rejoins the 'existentialist' problem in its very essence.

Revue Scientifique, November–December 1952.

---

[1] Into irreversibility. See 'La réflexion de l'Énergie'. (The Reflexion of Energy) (*Revue des Questions Scientifiques*, October 1952).

CHAPTER XXI

A DEFENCE OF ORTHOGENESIS IN THE MATTER OF PATTERNS OF SPECIATION

A *Genetics and Phyletics*

Thanks to the vast empirical researches pursued in biology in the last half-century, living matter is seen to *speciate*: that is to say that, abandoned to the reproductive mechanisms by which it multiplies, it does not merely break up into a host of isolated individuals but gradually collects itself, by the play of great numbers, around one or several dominant types: each group thus formed being liable, at the end of a certain time, to divide in its turn (with or without mutation but always statistically) into new zoological unities.

About this initial and elementary mechanism of the birth of species, successive generations continue to show and teach us much more. But what they absolutely cannot do (being unable to experiment, as is necessary, in million-year spans), and what palaeontology alone is capable of doing, is to determine the *patterns* formed by the forces of speciation acting over a very long period on a single quantum of living matter. By and large, the whole scientific world agrees in admitting that the design thus formed is essentially constituted of ramified and divergent segments. But whether on the internal structure and progressive transformation of these *phyla*, or – more important – on their inter-connections and the laws (if these exist) of their succession and mass distribution in the biosphere, our knowledge is still sporadic or rudimentary. Despite the enormous quantity of accumulated material and ideas in circulation, a *phyletics* worthy of the name has not yet been successfully formulated, as it should be, as an extension of modern *genetics*.

And why? Surely because biologists have not yet decided to attribute the same degree of reality (or a higher degree of reality even) to the effects of *orientated intensification* as to the effects of a *simple diversification* of characteristics, in the historical developments of evolution.

In order definitely to establish itself as a science (that is to say, in the final resort, to bring itself into harmonious line with the general laws of energetics) would it not be necessary for palaeontology, instead of seeking (as it is vainly trying to do at present!) to eliminate all idea of 'direction' in the genesis of species, to attempt on the contrary fully to integrate the so-called forces or factors of 'orthogenesis'[1] in its theories?

Such is the idea that has been growing in me for a long time, and that I wish to express here, once more.

B *Phyletic Phenomena of Diversification*

Starting from the initial appearance (well established by genetics) of certain elementary centres of assemblage and differentiation within any population in the course of multiplication, theoretically the most direct and simplest way of expressing and explaining the progress of speciation would obviously be to relate it to pure effects of extension and divergence, if that were possible.

Under the prolonged and magnifying influence of the milieu, eating habits, geographical distance, etc, it is easy to conceive that the elementary fibres experimentally recognized and reproduced by biologists in the laboratory have gradually collected in bundles of increasing thickness and divergence. Hence the morphological 'radiations' distinguished long ago in all zoological textbooks: terrestrial, aquatic, burrowing, winged forms; herbivorous, insectivorous, carnivorous types; specifically continental fauna, etc.

---

[1] This much disputed term is of course taken here in its etymological and most general sense of *directed* transformation (to whatever degree and under whatever influence, this 'direction' may manifest itself).

Thus to reduce the whole mystery of animal morphogenesis to a pure mechanism of *dispersion* would be all the more interesting because, as a result, the passage from micro- to macro-phenomena (that is to say from the genetic to the phyletic) in the field of speciation might then operate by a sort of direct 'integration'. Always the same mechanism in small and great alike. A charming perspective, of course, and one whose attraction certainly counts for a great deal in the present day tendency of the Neo-Darwinists (particularly in the United States)[1] who will not recognize in the history of living forms anything but a vast phenomenon, planetarily extended, of diversification pushed to its extreme. A principally (if not entirely) dispersive evolution, supported by no fundamental polarization (no curving) of the stuff of things.

This is exactly the perspective, described as 'new' (but should one not call it regressive?) against which I think it is important to react, by reintegrating a certain 'preferential' into the mere 'dice-play' – if we wish to save the greatness of the phenomenon of life.

c *Phyletic Phenomena of Intensification*

Whether or not – as I have just said – it is out of a spirit of imitation (or even of intimidation) in face of the success of genetics, one thing is certainly clear: that in the last twenty years no self-respecting palaeontologist has uttered the once classical word *orthogenesis* except with embarrassment or disdain.

I am of course the first to recognize that particular meanings were originally attached to this term (as to the term *evolution*) which seem to us unacceptable today: an almost magical straightness of the phyletic lines, implying certain vitalist or finalist conceptions which are decidedly out of date.

But there is a vast difference between correcting and rejecting.

Now, to take scientific account of the enormous edifice of living forms, as it gradually appears before our eyes throughout almost a

[1] See, for example, Patterns of Evolution, by Horace E. Wood, *Transactions of the New York Academy of Science*, 1954, pp. 324–64.

billion years of geological time, is it really possible to be content with 'numbers'? Or, in one way or another, must we not inevitably have recourse to *vectors* – that is to say *ipso facto* to reintroduce orthogenesis?

This, I believe, we must certainly do. The evidence for it is growing. Whether we consider the various phyla reconstituted by palaeontology (orthogenesis of forms), singly and in detail, or raise ourselves to the height from which we can observe in its totality (fundamental orthogenesis) the wave, which envelops the sum of the phyla constituting the complete biosphere at any moment; at whichever level we take our observations the necessity is the same.

1. *Orthogenesis of forms. Or: The morphological accentuation of animal species.* Thanks to an increasing number of excavations systematically sited at specially sensitive points of evolution,[1] palaeontologists have succeeded, in the last twenty or twenty-five years, in analysing the animal lines (the mammalian in particular) with some minuteness; and each time they have done so, the phyla have tended to give the impression of vanishing into mist. If we look at the picture of the proboscidians, drawn by Osborn, or that of the oreodontids by Schultz and Falkenbach, or that of the rhinocerotids by Horace E. Wood, it will seem at first sight that in the proliferation of neighbouring forms, each independent of the rest, orthogenesis vanishes like an illusion from the moment one tries to look at it closely. But surely (as in the case of a picture examined under a magnifying glass) to look at lines from too close produces distortion? If the enlargement is great, the diversification of features is, of course, exaggerated, and tends to mask the progressive accentuation of the characteristics in phylogenesis. But this accentuation is no less present, and infallibly

---

[1] And here I am thinking of the astonishing collections gradually amassed, prepared, catalogued and illustrated in Charles Frick's two laboratories in New York. Oreodontids, camelids, 'cynoid' carnivores, etc, present themselves in sheaves of types and species. The richest material in the world, perhaps, at this moment, for a systematic study of phyla, discovered in their earliest stages in the immediate neighbourhood of their point of emergence.

reappears on the collective picture the moment one puts oneself at the desired distance to observe it.

What does it matter, after all, if the genealogy of the equids, instead of being capable of representation as formerly by only two or three lines, has taken the form of a sheaf of more or less short and discontinuous fibres? From the moment when, above the fibres, the sheaf continues to exist, extending broadly from *Hyracotherium* to the *Equus* type, orthogenesis (even if disguised under the names of 'trend' or 'ortho-selection') continues to function. It is not – it could not be – exorcised.

The dominant feature in the phylogenesis of the best-known groups is not, in the last resort, the dispersion but the *canalization* of forms.

This is a proof that, followed along major tracts of time, chromosomic characteristics are not the inert 'grains' and 'isotropes' that geneticists suppose, but in fact elementary vectors, consisting of very short orientated segments, reacting additively, always in a single favoured direction, to the complex 'topography' of the geographical and biological milieu in which they find themselves.

No 'mysticism' (whatever my friend M. W. Wood may say) is implied in the recognition of this phenomenon which inevitably reminds us of the entirely material phenomenon of a river gradually establishing its course to conform with the terrain over which it flows.

But just as, in the example I have chosen of a river tracing its bed, there is (whatever the breadth and form of the basin under consideration), the same *gravity* acting everywhere and always on the flowing water; so in the case of 'speciating' matter also (that is to say in order to explain the formation of any phylum), is there not – must we not inevitably postulate – the existence of a single basic factor in operation?

2. *Fundamental orthogenesis. Or: The cosmic drift of Complexity/Consciousness.* Placed symbolically in a single diagram, the innumerable phyla today recognized by palaeontology invariably distribute them-

selves under all circumstances along a multitude of radii pointing in all directions: each phylum therefore is conceivably capable of definition by a certain azimuth marking its position and orientation in relation to the system as a whole.

From this point of view one might say that life, in its fumbling advances, behaves very like a wave spreading up the beach. Truly, it seems to have *tried everything*.

But is it not more remarkable still, when one thinks of it, that along any of the azimuths under consideration, it has constantly been *trying in a single direction* – that is to say towards greater arrangement and psychism, one by means of the other, simultaneously?

A general drift of complexity/consciousness'[1] drawing the corpuscular stuff of the universe globally (whatever its diversification of detail) towards ever more improbable states of organization and interiorization. Palaeontologists are as yet only mildly interested in this anonymous movement of cosmic scale (a movement which complements, perhaps even compensates thermo-dynamic entropy). They are much less interested in fact than the physicists.[2] But yet, since it is they, the palaeontologists, who first detected the existence and can alone continue to inform us on the historical details of the phenomenon, is it not their principal task to exploit their discovery to the uttermost?

Willingly or unwillingly, palaeontology is, and cannot help becoming increasingly the *science of orthogenesis*, which it must consider both in its general, fundamental drift and in the various branches into which it divides in the course of its route.

And from this point of view it pleases me to imagine the birth and development of a true 'geobiology', as an extension of geophysics and

[1] A drift especially marked, as might be expected, in the youngest and most active zones of the biosphere (vertebrates), in which it can be conveniently measured in terms of the developments and concentration of the nervous system; but a drift already recognizable, in fact, in the atomization of energy and the moleculization of the atom.

[2] See, for example, E. Schrödinger, *What is Life?* (Cambridge, 1945) Harold F. Blum *Time's Arrow and Evolution* (Princeton University Press, 1951); François Meyer, *Problématique de l'Evolution* (Paris, 1954).

geochemistry, carrying out ever more thorough studies in the field between general speciation and hominization.

Indisputably everything happens in biogenesis as if man (despite a host of accidental characteristics which make him 'one of many' among the other animals) formed a single phylum on earth along which the two orthogeneses, formal and fundamental, as I have defined them above by purely phenomenal criteria, sensibly coincide (in the direction of maximum cerebration).

It is now our business to utilize this natural and significant coincidence scientifically.

On the one hand, by the light of events in ourselves, in the realm of *reflected* transformations and inventions, to interpret, in nature present and past, the formation, distribution and progress of the various phyla within the biosphere.

And on the other hand, inversely, by extending the curves plotted by palaeontology, to try and guess what is taking place in us, self-evolutionarily, beneath the double veil of technical socialization and co-reflexion.

Man illuminating from within the cosmic mechanism of orthogenesis; and orthogenesis, in return, throwing light from without on the human zoological future.

These are, if I am not mistaken, reduced to their essentials, the function and programme imposed by the present state of our knowledge on the palaeontology of tomorrow.

Unpublished, January 1955. P. Teilhard de Chardin had written these pages as a contribution to the symposium that M. Jean Piveteau was planning for April 1955.

INDEX

INDEX